Date Due

T102			
T101			
T47			

THE TOAD
IS THE
EMPEROR'S UNCLE

THE TOAD IS THE EMPEROR'S UNCLE

ANIMAL FOLKTALES FROM VIET-NAM

TOLD AND ILLUSTRATED BY **VO-DINH**

Doubleday & Company, Inc., Garden City, New York

Library of Congress Catalog Card Number 72-103783
Copyright © 1970 by Sung Ngo-Dinh
All Rights Reserved
Printed in the United States of America
First Edition

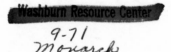

For my daughters
PHÙNG-NAM and
LINH. GIANG

CONTENTS

AUTHOR'S NOTE

Life in traditional Viet-Nam is rural and harmonious. While the small ruling class was, for centuries, made up of learned men —scholars, poets, painters, and musicians—the great majority of Viet-Namese are craftsmen and farmers. Their existence, like that of their counterparts in other lands, is one of unceasing labor and simple joys.

One of these joys is retelling their great wealth of folk tales. Adults and children alike delight in them. Not only are they repeated over and over again to children at bedtime, as folk tales usually are, but later they are taught in school. It is no wonder that the character and beliefs of the Viet-Namese, as well as the nature of the country itself, are reflected in these stories.

By the age of ten or so, like all other Viet-Namese children, I knew a number of my country's folk tales. Now, years later, I still remember most of them vividly. The tales have a way of incorporating themselves into our native language. We think "eel eyes" ("The Eel and the Porgy") when we see narrow, untrustworthy eyes. We say *"Ngau* rain" ("The Ravens Build a Bridge") when it rains heavily, and *"Da-Trang* effort" ("The Sand-Carrier Crab") when we see someone working hard at some hopeless task.

The climate of Viet-Nam, too, is a good reminder of our folk tales. A tropical land with cool, dry winters and hot, humid summers, Viet-Nam needs great quantities of water for rice growing. Anyone who has ever seen a July downpour there will not forget it, a true deluge! as in "The Toad Is the Emperor's Uncle" and "The Carp That Became a Dragon." Also, the wide variety of animals found in this collection is indicative of the terrain of the country: Viet-Nam is flanked on the west by jungle (elephants, tigers, big snakes) and on the east by the sea (crabs, squid). Between the mountains and the sea stretch the lowlands where most Viet-Namese live, and where the water buffalo is undoubtedly the best-loved animal of all.

Like rural people everywhere, the Viet-Namese live close to animals, regarding them more often as friends and co-workers than as pets. Buffalos help plow fields, roosters are living alarm clocks, dogs guard homes. Fish have a secure place in Viet-Namese affections for they, more than cattle or fowl, are the main source of protein. In the title story, the ordinary, ugly toad, whose sole usefulness is eating flies and mosquitoes, is made the principal hero, accomplishing what man cannot. In "The Tiger's Stripes," the quiet and indispensable water buffalo remains true to character, a model of faithfulness. In the story bearing its name, the minuscule fly somehow manages to find its place, too.

But the use of animal heroes in folk tales does more than illustrate a fondness for living creatures. As Aesop and La Fontaine also knew, the fate of an animal can teach, in a witty and lively fashion, some important moral. But although the lessons implied in these Viet-Namese tales may sometimes be similar to those in stories from more western lands, they stem from a totally different source: the deep influence that Buddhism, Confucianism and Taoism have had on the Viet-Namese character.

For example, one of the five cardinal virtues taught by Confucianism is: *Nghia,* which means both loyalty and gratitude. Since the snake in "The Snake and Its Benefactor" is neither grateful nor loyal to its master, it deserved its fate, the story says. On the contrary, even though he had been condemned to life-long servitude, the horse in "The Horse and the Eighteen Bandits" regained his liberty by fulfilling his duty of *Nghia.* The importance of *Nghia* is expressed in other tales: by the crow in "The Crow's Pearl," the snake in "The Sand-Carrier Crab." Still other stories remind us of the Confucian virtues of hard work ("The Ravens Build a Bridge"), courage and determination ("The Carp That Became a Dragon"), and common sense ("The Eel and the Porgy.")

As a religion whose aim is to help man attain true wisdom and freedom, Buddhism strongly influences Viet-Namese thinking. The Buddha taught that life is a cycle of birth, age, sickness, and death, filled with desire and unfulfillment, that the life we are living now is the result of our preceding life, and our next life will be determined by how we are living our present one. By meditation, wisdom and charity, we are able, however, to break this eternal cycle and to become truly free. This belief is fully illustrated in "The Horse and the Eighteen Bandits."

Although the role of Taoism in Viet-Namese life is less evident than that of Buddhism or Confucianism, the doctrine (taught by Lao-Tse, a sixth-century B.C. Chinese philosopher) has deeply affected the Viet-Namese people. Modern science echoes what Lao-Tse himself taught: life is short and the earth is only a tiny dot in the infinite universe. So for Lao-Tse it was most important to have a simple life and a peaceful heart. The rich man in "The Little Lizard's Sorrow" has everything but a carefree existence. His wiser visitor prefers to be poor but free. In "The Crow's Pearl," the former buffalo-boy may have everything, including a happy old age, but when he dies, the source of his fortune disappears. Thus we see why the average Viet-Namese, though he loves life and work, has deep in his heart an unusual detachment from earthly existence and possessions.

Reading these stories, we might conclude that the Viet-Namese are a rather serious people. They are not so by any means. Like people everywhere in the world, the Viet-Namese can be, at times, irreverent and humorous. The Jade Emperor is their revered, supreme ruler of heaven and earth. Yet whenever a Viet-Namese sees a toad hopping by, he exclaims: "There goes the Emperor's Uncle!" In the title story all the animals, except the tiger, are those seen daily. Yet ordinary as they are, they are able to give the heavenly gods a rough time. And in "That Fourth Leg of the Dog" the compassionate Buddha is revered, loved, and mocked all at once. The irreverent villager in "A Cat Is a Cat Is a Cat" seems disrespectful enough when he decides on the name for his prized pet. While finding it amusing, his best friend decides, nonetheless, that he must be taught a lesson.

There is one other important trait of the Viet-Namese people which several stories in this collection reveal. As neighbors to colossal China for over two thousand years, managing to survive without being absorbed by her, the Viet-Namese have apparently learned the lessons of "The Clever Earthworm" and "The Eel and the Porgy"—that intelligence and cleverness can be superior to material wealth and physical strength. With ruse, the Viet-Namese like to think, a hare can beat a tiger, and a little boy, as in "The Fly," can dupe a powerful, rich man. Or, as in "Dragons?" even an obscure but clever dabbler can put one over on a famous artist whose skill is without compare.

THE TOAD
IS
THE EMPEROR'S UNCLE

◉◉◉◉◉

Since ancient times, in Viet-Nam, the children have been singing a funny little song:

Con Cóc Là Cậu ông Trời,
Ai mà đánh cóc thì Trời đánh cho !

which means:

> "The toad is the Emperor's uncle,
> Don't ever hurt the toad, or His Majesty will hurt you!"

The toad, the lowly, warty toad, uncle of the Jade Emperor, supreme ruler of Heaven and Earth? Viet-Namese children believe he is.

ONE YEAR, a long time ago, the country was ravaged by drought. It was the most terrifying one that had ever come to the land. No one knew what had happened to the Rain-God, but he certainly was neglecting the duties assigned to him by the Emperor. Ten thousand creatures were suffering cruelly: plants were drying out, men and animals grew weaker each day, and many were even dying from thirst.

The toad, deep in his hole, was better off than most for he did not need much water to survive. Nonetheless, what he saw around him made him very angry at the Rain-God and the

Emperor. He decided that, lowly as he was, he would set out for the sky and give the heavenly rulers a piece of his mind.

As soon as he started out, he met a wasp. At the insect's inquiry, the toad told him the purpose of his journey.

"Well," the wasp said, "would you care if I accompany you? A bit of juice would be enough for me but I cannot even get that! Look at the flowers; they are dry like autumn leaves. Let me go with you, for I want to tell the Emperor, myself, what I think of him." The toad agreed to the wasp's proposal, and the two of them set off together.

They had not gone very far before they met a large tiger. They could not remember when they had last seen him looking so pitiful. Dying from thirst, the tiger nonetheless managed a nice big roar and asked the travelers where they were heading. When the tiger learned of their plan, he also asked to go along and was promptly accepted. The tiger was so helpful that he let the toad hold on to his tail so they could journey faster to the sky.

By and by, they met a rooster. "Hello there! Where are the three of you going?" the rooster crowed.

Being a fast talker, the wasp hurried to answer for his companions. "Don't you see what a drought there is?" the wasp buzzed. "We are going to bring our case to the Emperor who must bear the responsibility for all our miseries."

Flapping his large, flaming wings, the rooster shrieked: "I want to go along! I want to go along! I live on rice and corn but this drought has only brought gravels and stones."

Running, flying, the toad, the wasp, the tiger, and the rooster set out for the long journey together. Their anger made them all forget that they were as thirsty as the dry, cracked surface of the rice fields.

The trip was long, but at last they arrived at the gates of the heavenly palace. The wise old toad, who was by now the leader of the group, said to his companions: "You three just stay where you are and keep quiet. Let me handle everything. When I need you, I will call you. But remember, only the one called should come!"

"All right, brother Toad, it is understood," the tiger, the wasp, and the rooster said together, and they remained hidden outside the gates.

After having backed far away from the walls, the toad started running, running, gathering speed and momentum, and in one broad jump, landed right in the middle of the table where His Majesty the Emperor was sipping his morning tea. Staring at the heavenly ruler, the little toad rolled his protruding eyes and expanded his enormous cheeks. He tried to look fearsome, and quite nasty did he appear.

Startled and angered by such insolence, the Emperor banged the table and thundered: "Who do you think you are, miserable ugly toad? Is that how you behave in my sacred palace?" But the toad, saying nothing, only kept rolling his eyes and staring at the Emperor who became very red in the face.

"Well! He does not even deign to answer me!" the Emperor thundered again. "Soldiers! Throw this horrid creature out of here!"

But then, swiftly, the toad raised himself on his legs and croaked at the top of his lungs: "Brother Wasp, where are you?"

The wasp flew in like a streak of lightning and began to sting the soldiers, who ran howling in all directions.

Seeing that he needed more help, the Emperor commanded: "Come now, my Heavenly Dog! Tear this toad to pieces!"

A terrible beast sprang out. He looked like a gigantic wolf with a lion's mane and the tail of an alligator.

"Brother Tiger! Come to my help!" the toad screamed.

It was a battle worth watching, even for the Emperor. The tiger, more expert at fighting and encouraged by the toad's deafening croaks, soon had the upper hand and, crushing the Heavenly Dog under his forepaws, he sank his fangs into his attacker's throat.

By this time, the Emperor was very worried. He raised his large silk sleeves and commanded: "Thunder and Lightning!"

The wind began to blow strongly and the god of Thunder and Lightning appeared with his fork and his fire. But at the toad's summons, the rooster was already there to meet the god. Wings flapping, claws swinging, the rooster made good use of his formidable, steely beak. Dropping his fork, the terrible god could do nothing but cover his head with his arms to prevent the rooster from pecking out his eyes.*

Seeing that it was time for a truce, the Emperor told the toad, with more respect this time: "All right, Uncle Toad,† tell your friends to stop massacring my subjects! But pray, inform me, why is it you came up here?"

With a touch of sarcasm, the toad answered: "Your Majesty could certainly have asked me that a moment earlier." He then turned to his friends and ordered them to stop fighting. "That is enough for now!" he said to the animals. "Come here and testify to the truth of my statements."

---

*It is popularly believed that the Thunder and Lightning god has always been afraid of roosters whose bones are made of the god's bones.

†In Viet-Nam, you call a man uncle, even though he is not a relative, when you wish him to know that you hold him in respect and affection.

When the Emperor heard the animals' complaint, he summoned the Rain-God and reprimanded him severely: "Your task
is to see that all creatures have enough water to live. You have,
however, neglected your duties and will be punished accord-
ingly. Look at what four earthly animals can do to disturb my
heavenly palace!"

Smashing his forehead against the jade dais where the Emperor was seated, the Rain-God begged for mercy: "I pray that
Your Majesty will be so just as to reconsider. The world is immense, the water all creatures need is limitless. But I am all by
myself and despite my vigilance, cannot attend to every part of
the world at once. . . . " But with a wave of his tubby foreleg, the
toad interrupted the unhappy god:

"You can or you cannot, that is your own concern! We down
there on earth need water to survive." Then he turned to the
Emperor: "Now that Your Majesty knows our wants and what
we can do if they are not satisfied, I am sure that he would not
wish us to come up again for another visit." Rolling his protruding eyes and staring hard at the Emperor, the toad added, with
a hint of a threat in his voice:

"From now on, please remember, any time that water is low
on earth, I will simply begin croaking and you will order the
Rain-God to bring water down to us. It is agreed and understood,
is it not?"

Fearful now of the toad and his invincible companions, the
Emperor hurriedly accepted this suggestion. "Oh, yes," he re-
assured the toad. "Oh yes, Uncle Toad, you can be certain of that
and go back to Earth in peace. I will see to it that you have your
rain when you want it. Yes, you will have your rain when you
want it!" All smiles and benevolence, the Emperor bade the

animals farewell, and heaved a big sigh when the four of them disappeared behind the heavenly gates.

It is no wonder that today, as everybody must have noticed, whenever one hears the toad croaking, rain comes almost instantly. It is obvious that the Emperor has been living up to his promise.

FATHER CATFISH

◎◎◎◎◎◎

To other fish, the catfish is indeed unusual. Not because of his whiskers: after all, cats have whiskers too. It is the catfish's head which really intrigues and even bothers them. Instead of being flat vertically, the way the porgy, bass, sole, and whatnots' heads are, this strange fish's head is flat horizontally. Once, despite his ferocious-looking whiskers and prickly fins, somebody told him that he looked as if his head had been sat upon by an absent-minded hippopotamus. That was enough to send the catfish into a terrible fit of temper. The joke was, after all, partly true!

ONE YEAR in early spring, when the catfish still had his round head, the pond was swarming with tiny tadpoles. During a stroll, the catfish stopped to admire them as they darted about in the water, frolicking as if the whole world belonged to them.

"They do look very much like me, don't they?" the catfish thought, feeling a twinge of pride which made his whiskers quiver with excitement. "Perhaps I could herd them away to my house and keep them with me; yes, perhaps I could! Everybody would simply think that they are my own children. They look so much like me. The same smooth head, the same supple body, the same delicate tail, the same deep gray-black coloring. . . ." The catfish looked at the tadpoles, then looked at himself and already felt like a father. "And how Madame Catfish would love them," he thought.

The catfish made up his mind. A moment later, the band of

little tadpoles, shepherded by their adopted father catfish, went to live in their new home at the other end of the pond.

The catfish's joy at being a father, however, was heart-rending tragedy for poor Mother Toad. When she discovered after a hunting expedition that her tadpoles were gone, she screamed and cried and hopped wildly about in search of her children. Nobody seemed to know what had happened to them except, finally, a kindly old turtle.

"Mr. Turtle, have you by any chance seen my children?" Mother Toad yelled to him as soon as she saw him.

"Seen your children? I have been everywhere looking for you. They are gone. They are gone."

"What do you mean they are gone? Oh, my dearest ones, where are you?" Mother Toad began to wail at the top of her lungs.

"Now, now, calm down and I will tell you everything," the turtle commanded, and tell her everything he did. The turtle had happened to see the catfish take the tadpoles away, but not being a relative of theirs, could not bring himself to get into a row with such a formidable villain.

The turtle advised Mother Toad to bring her case to the mandarin who governed the pond.

The day of trial arrived. Escorted by soldiers, the warlike catfish made his appearance at the court, convinced that everybody would believe his statement that the little tadpoles were his own children, so much like him did they look. But encouraged by the turtle, who now acted as her witness, Mother Toad went on accusing the catfish of kidnaping her offspring.

It was quite a dilemma for the mandarin-judge. On the one hand, the little ones lived and swam in the water and indeed looked more like the catfish than the toad who lived on land. On the other hand, the toad's seemingly genuine unhappiness and the testimony of the reliable turtle made the mandarin wonder. Not wanting to rush things, he adjourned the hearings with an order to return in two months for a new trial. By that time, the little tadpoles had completed their transformation and, leaving their tails in the water, had jumped to solid ground.

When the catfish realized that it was futile to pretend innocence any longer, he fled, but the mandarin's soldiers waylaid him and brought him to court at the appointed hour. Facing the warring parties and the audience, the judge pronounced the catfish guilty.

"You should be ashamed of yourself," he admonished the catfish, "for such a nasty act. You have caused Madame Toad much too great an unhappiness! The court rules that your whiskers, your fins and your tail be cut off. But, in consideration of your wife's love for the little tadpoles and of the care she gave them while they stayed with you, I am willing to reduce your sentence. Soldiers! Give him twenty strokes of the cane on his head!"

That day, bleeding and shaken, the catfish returned home and Madame Catfish barely recognized him: twenty blows of the cane had flattened his head like a pancake.

No wonder that since then the catfish has made only rare appearances. He suddenly developed a taste for staying flat in the depths of the pond, burrowing himself under the mud. His temper, too, has not improved any since his unfortunate adventure.

THE SNAKE
AND
ITS BENEFACTOR

◎◎◎◎◎

The central part of a traditional Viet-Namese house, a kind of sitting room, is dominated by an altar which is consecrated to the cult of the ancestors, or to that of the Lord Buddha or, more often than not, to both cults. The middle of the altar is occupied by a large bronze urn where incense is burned, flanked on both sides by a bronze crane standing on a turtle. There are several explanations as to what the cranes and the turtles symbolize. This story is only one of them.

THERE WAS once a poor man who, living alone, kept as a pet a very large snake whom he loved dearly. All his spare time was spent trying to catch frogs, toads, or small fish for his pet. Sometimes the man even went so far as to bring a baby chick to his snake for he knew his fondness for bird meat.

But, it happened that one day the man could not catch anything and, having not a penny, could not afford to buy chickens either. He tried to feed the snake some of his own rice but the latter refused to eat it and instead threw a terrible fit of temper.

When the man again came home empty-handed, the snake hissed at him:

"You incapable man! It is now the second day I have not had anything in my stomach. Why, I am going to swallow you up yourself and see what you taste like!"

The man suddenly became fearful of his angry, vicious pet. But ashamed of not being able to feed him, the kind man was almost willing to offer himself up as a meal to the reptile. He realized, however, that the beast was horribly ungrateful: the man had saved him, still a baby snake, from the iron claws of a rooster and had brought him up like a good father. Greatly puzzled, the man said, scratching his head:

"Well, my dear snake, if you want to eat me, you have a very good reason to do so. But I don't know. . . . It seems such a shame that I should die just because you haven't got those few frogs that escaped from my hands! I suppose we could ask what the other animals think of this. They will certainly understand you better than I, and they might approve of your decision to eat me up. If they do, I will immediately oblige."

So, the poor man and his pet went out of the house. They soon met a beautiful tall crane standing in the deep water of a rice field. When the crane had been told of the visitors' problem, he turned to the snake and scolded him:

"Scoundrel! How can you ever think such thoughts? How can you ever look at your master again without shame? This man has saved your life, has brought you up like a child of his own, has lovingly fed you with delicacies! And now, for the sake of your miserable stomach, you are prepared to eat your benefactor. That is sheer cruelty and ingratitude. You must now lie low and beg your master's forgiveness!" Unshaken, the snake barely waited for the crane to finish his sermon before he urged his master to leave with him.

A turtle was the next animal they met. How pleased the snake was when, having been told everything, the turtle said in a scratchy, subterranean voice: "What? What? My poor man, if you keep a pet and cannot feed him, it is only natural that he eat you! What is there to complain about?"

It was now the man's turn to urge that they go on. Soon they met a big black crow. The man said to the bird:

"Master Crow, we would like to have your wise counsel on a certain matter. Snake here has been my pet now for many years; I have kept and fed him since he was as long as three fingers. But for two days now I have not been able to catch any frogs for him and he is dying from hunger and he wants to eat me. Do you think I should give myself up as a meal to my snake?"

The crow looked thoughtful but did not answer. Suddenly, he pounced on the snake. With a few swift strokes of his sharp beak, he pecked and scratched him to death.

Dead but undaunted, the snake carried his case all the way to the Lord Buddha. How disappointed the snake's soul was when it heard the Enlightened One pronounce this judgment: "The crane was right in admonishing you, Snake, for gratitude is among the first virtues. The turtle was wrong and has proved himself an unscrupulous character. I therefore order the people, from now on, to fashion objects of worship in their images: the noble crane is permitted to stand on the callous turtle's back. As for you, Snake, you owed your life and your daily food to your master but you were willing to give him death. Do you not think you deserved what the crow did to you?"

Since then, during periods of worship or festivities in honor of their ancestors or of the Lord Buddha, the Viet-Namese never fail to burn incense in the bronze urn, on both sides of which a bronze crane stands on the back of a turtle. Outside, usually in front of their house near the garden gate, they erect a very tall bamboo pole. The crow, made of black straw or paper, stands on the very top, and right below it, fluttering in the wind, a thin strip of white cloth has been tied, symbolizing the ungrateful dead snake.

THE RAVENS
BUILD A BRIDGE

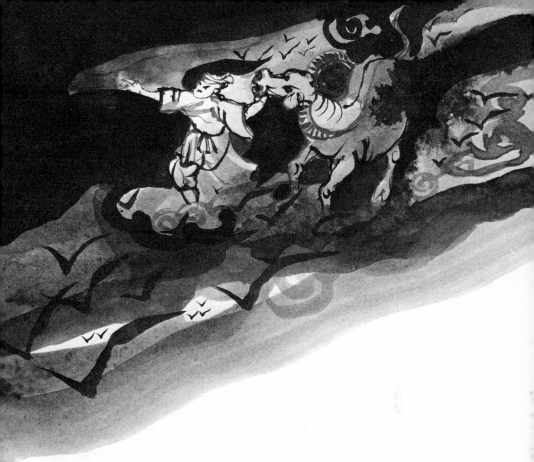

UP IN the sky, life was just as on earth. There was a ruler, the Jade Emperor, who was served by the gods, much like the Viet-Namese king and his mandarins. Then there were the heavenly people who kept busy at their occupations very much like their earthly counterparts. It happened that Ngau-Lang, a handsome shepherd, and Chuc-Nu, a beautiful girl whose duty was weaving silk for the Imperial Palace, fell deeply in love. They begged the Jade Emperor to allow them to marry. Permission was given with the condition that they were not to neglect their respective responsibilities.

Alas, in their exuberant happiness, the young people forgot the agreement. Ngau-Lang's buffalos, noticing his distraction, ran wild in the heavenly fields while Chuc-Nu's weaving equipment grew white with spider webs.

When the Jade Emperor learned of this, he became very angry and ordered the young people to be banished to the Silver River, that long white gathering of stars which Western people call the Milky Way. The punishment was indeed harsh. Ngau-Lang was condemned to live on one bank of the river while Chuc-Nu had to stay on the other. They were, moreover, permitted to cross the river to see each other only once a year, on the seventh day of the seventh lunar month.

As it happened, there was not, oddly enough, a single bridge over the Silver River. So, to make it easier for Ngau-Lang and Chuc-Nu to cross it on their yearly visit, the Jade Emperor ordered the carpenters and the masons to build one. The chosen workmen, however, turned out to be a poor lot: bickering and quarreling, they never got around to finishing the bridge on that first seventh day of the seventh month. Angered, the Jade Emperor punished them by transforming them into ravens. The birds were condemned to fly over the Silver River every year on that day, holding each other by wing and tail, to form a live bridge.

Chuc-Nu, however, was a very dainty young lady. She had never had a very high opinion of those noisy black ravens that were reputed to delight in the consumption of the dead. She gathered her courage and begged the Jade Emperor for a favor which was granted. Every year thereafter, at the seventh lunar month—at least in Viet-Nam—the ravens quarrel so hard with each other (just as when they were still carpenters and masons) that quantities of their feathers fall off and their heads become bald. The reason for it all is that, once shed of their outer feathers, the ravens are ready, clean and new, for Chuc-Nu to walk on them without soiling her feet as she goes to meet her husband.

To this day, at every yearly reunion, Ngau-Lang and Chuc-Nu are so happy to see each other again that they cannot help crying. They cry so abundantly that every year on the seventh day of the seventh lunar month, the rain never fails to fall in Viet-Nam. Needing much water for their rice fields, the farmers consider the couple's tears a heavenly blessing and wish they would meet more often.

THE
CLEVER
EARTH WORM

◎◎◎◎◎

Of all living creatures, few seem as lowly as the earthworm. No wings, no legs, no antenna, no fur, no scales. With his head, his tail and his body looking alike, the earthworm only inspires indifference or pity. However, those who know the following story have quite a different opinion of him.

ONE DAY, a man caught a little earthworm and used him as bait for fishing. Hooked at the end of the line, our poor little worm wriggled and wriggled, miserable and fearful that death was certain.

A fish stopped by and stared at him, its jaws moving eagerly. The little earthworm managed to stay still for a moment so as not to excite the fish and asked: "Mister Fish, dear sir, do you see what is right above my back?"

With his mouth half-opened and ready to pounce on the earthworm, the big fish stopped dead in his course.

"What?" the fish answered in astonishment. "What? I don't see anything but water!"

"Well, dear sir, that's a fishing line. A man up there is trying to catch *you,*" the earthworm said, and, trying to look as sad as he could, he went on, "You see, I really do not have any regret in leaving this world, considering my miserable existence, always crawling and hiding beneath the ground, despised by everybody, man and beast alike. I would be only too happy to give myself up to you, for I see that it would please you. But, oh, sir!" the worm's voice was choked with emotion. "But, oh, sir! I would hate to see somebody like yourself be caught. You who are so strong, so beautiful, who can go wherever you want, whose scales shine like jewels, whose eyes gleam like stars! To think that for the sake of tasting a bit of miserable food like myself, you can be caught and scaled and opened up and served on a plate for the pleasure of man, I cannot help but cry. . . ." Thereupon, the earthworm began weeping copiously, his translucent little body shaking all over.

The fish stared at the worm for a long second, smacking his lips and waving his tail, but inside he trembled a bit at the thought of serving himself up as dinner to the man above. Regretfully, he backed away from the worm and slowly disappeared.

No sooner had he gone than another fish appeared and looked as if he, too, were going to swallow the bait. But the little worm began to tell him the same story and the second fish also departed. This happened again and again until the fisherman, tired of trying, pulled the worm from the water and, taking him off the hook, threw him away.

The little earthworm, at last free, hastened to burrow into the soil and a few seconds later, disappeared from sight.

THE EEL
AND
THE PORGY

◎◎◎◎◎

A Viet-Namese proverb warns us to beware of people whose eyes are small and narrow like those of an eel. There are, of course, many good and kind people who just don't have large eyes. But this is something the Viet-Namese porgy, a red-eyed, fresh-water fish, finds hard to believe.

ONE DAY, long ago, when the porgy's eyes were not yet red, he went out for a walk and met an eel. As soon as he saw him, the porgy twisted his tail and began heading in another direction. He had never liked that slippery fellow. But it was too late. The eel called to him: "Wait a minute, friend Porgy, what is the hurry? Come on in my house for a moment!" Reluctantly, the porgy obliged, knowing that the eel had not invited him to stop for a chat because he liked him but because he wanted to show off his new house.

It was some house. Big and round like a medium-sized barrel, made of bamboo strips tied together at both ends. Coiling comfortably inside it, the snakelike fish peered out at passersby from his dark, unctuous, slippery self.

The porgy forced a smile that looked more like a grimace: "Well, good day, friend Eel! What a beautiful new house you built yourself!"

"This is just my summer residence, you know," the eel said, quite modestly. "Come on in. Very cool in here."

"Well, some other time, friend, I've got to go now. I was just running . . ." The porgy tried to get away. But the eel interrupted him with a flicker of his small head: "Now, now, you are not in any hurry. Come in for just a little talk. I've got something very important to tell you."

The porgy gulped. A funny sensation ran through his spine. Now that he had seen the eel's new house more closely, something in its appearance frightened him, but he just could not figure out why. It seemed to him he had seen houses like this somewhere. He did not like its look at all.

The eel was at the door, a perfect host: "You look wonderful, friend Porgy. You have changed so much since the last time we met. Why, your scales now look as if they are pure mother-of-pearl!"

The porgy was pleased. "Not so bad a fellow, this eel," he thought. He tried to look at himself but he could not. All he saw was his own tail.

"Heavens!" the eel exclaimed. "If only I could get just a bit of color like yours! Being the way I am . . ." The porgy stopped the eel, too kind to let him go on.

"But you, also, you look great! So black, so shiny!" The porgy suddenly felt all his apprehension vanish like smoke. Armed with a new appreciation for the eel, he entered his friend's house.

At once, in a flash, he remembered. The inside of the eel's house was nothing but the inside of a fishtrap: the opening was bristling with sharp bamboo sticks, their points converging toward him. In terror, he tried frantically to get out but it was to no avail. Each time he plunged toward the opening, the spikes hit his head. After a while, the poor porgy gave up and broke down crying. He cried so much over his deadly mistake that his eyes became all red while, free outside, undulating, darting, here and there, the heartless eel laughed and laughed. Never before had he so thoroughly enjoyed playing a trick.

The porgy cried so much his eyes stayed red, and the eel laughed so much his eyes got narrower and narrower until they were no larger than the head of a pin. Today, as we all know, their descendants still carry the same characteristics. Apparently, the unknown, kind fisherman, moved by the porgy's tears, had thrown him back into the river!

THE CARP
THAT BECAME
A DRAGON

◎◎◎◎◎

IT WAS the Rain-God's duty to bring water to earth. Somehow or other, he never managed to discharge his responsibilities with the abundance and promptness people expected of him. Therefore, the Jade Emperor decided one day to give him some assistance: he would create dragons. These creatures would live in clouds and thunder, on high mountains, and at the bottom of deep rivers. They were to absorb the water available in these places, store it inside their bodies and spurt it out whenever the need arose. Ancient water tanks, that is what dragons were to be.

The King of the Waters was then ordered to organize a competition among all aquatic creatures. Each was to attempt to cross over three divine waves formed by the Jade Emperor. The one who completed this dangerous journey would be transformed into the first dragon and worshiped by people everywhere.

A whole month went by, but not one of the water creatures had made it. Each one tried and tried but was crushed or swept away by the very first terrible wave.

Then the ordinary porgy, who had been too shy to enter the contest until now, decided that after all it would do him no harm to try. Amazingly, he shot through the first wave and plummeted into the trough, breathless but unscratched. Hardly had he recovered his senses when he felt himself sucked up higher than the clouds, higher than the sun itself, and hurled back on the clawlike foam of the second gargantuan crest. Though he failed, the porgy had gone farther than any other creature. And that is why, even today, a black dot can still be

seen at each side of the porgy: it was the good mark given him
by the Jade Emperor.

Seeing that the porgy had achieved some success, the lowly,
tiny shrimp plucked up all his courage for a swim. Beyond
everyone's expectation, one wave, then two waves smashed over
his little back and the shrimp still continued. But the third and
last one, the highest and deepest, smashed on him so hard that
the brave shrimp broke his back which, not surprisingly, has
remained curled ever since.

The last day of the competition arrived. Both the Jade Emperor
and the King of the Waters were very disappointed with the
creatures' abilities. At twilight, the sky filled with heavy black
clouds. The wind began to blow, thunder rolled from one end
of heaven to the other. The water rose up until the three waves
became more dense, more formidable than ever. It was only then
that the retiring carp made up his mind and entered the contest.

Looking back and forth, left and right, the fish found that
he was all by himself. Only the heaving dark sea was facing him.
The immense first wave was poised for its terrible assault. The
carp closed his eyes, and plunged. And plunged and plunged.
All he was aware of then was that his body seemed to be pulver-
ized into a million pieces. Water and water and water. Thunderous currents slashed at him, in front, at the sides, above, under.
The crossing was interminable. But then the carp found that
the first wave was gone. The second wave, higher, deeper than
the first, was already roaring at him and again he rode it. And
now, fins spread wide, tail flapping, scales flashing, he swam
across the top of the third water fortress. This last wave was as
high as Heaven itself! Riding its silver crest, the carp had a
quick glimpse of the Jade Emperor sitting on his golden throne,

surrounded by the gods and attendants. But the last wave did not come down as the two first had done. Instead, it rose higher and higher until the carp came face to face with Heaven's immense Rain Gates which gleamed with the colors of the rainbow. With one more stroke, he lurched forward and entered the realm of the gods. At once, the carp's body stretched out, long, long, long. His fins hardened quickly into scale-covered legs with sharp, curled claws. A pair of long horns sprang up on his elongated forehead.

The first dragon had appeared in the world.

If examined carefully, the dragons one sees in Oriental paintings and decorations reveal amazing similarities with the obscure carp, their ancestor: the same round, rainbow-hued scales, the same proud whiskers, the same protruding eyes . . . All in all, the carp looks so much like the dragon that some people in Vietnam are reluctant to eat the carp, although its meat is delicious. They probably don't want to run the risk of depriving Heaven of another rain-making dragon!

THE HARE
AND
THE TIGER

ONE DAY, a long, long time ago, all animals in the air and on land sent their representatives to a meeting, the purpose of which was to choose their leaders.

Not surprisingly, the powerful and noble eagle became King of the Birds. Somebody had merely suggested it and it was agreed without a single dissenting voice.

The land animals, however, had more difficulty agreeing with each other. The lordly lion seemed to be the inevitable choice except for two other contenders: the strong tiger and the huge elephant. The former argued that he was as strong if not stronger than the lion himself, and the latter pleaded that his bulk was without any doubt more appropriate for a king. The lion proposed that the two candidates compete with each other. He would simply take on the winner.

As both tiger and elephant were exceedingly proud of their powerful roars and not particularly anxious for a real fight with claws and tusks, they agreed that the duel should be more civilized than usual. With witnesses, they would go into the jungle and there, in turn, they would roar at the top of their lungs. The one whose vocal prowess did not succeed in making leaves fall off the branches would admit defeat and lie down for the other to kill him.

The huge elephant began first. His roar was so loud it was heard for miles around. Birds flew, animals and insects scurried in panic. But only one, no, two miserable leaves fell.

Then it was the tiger's turn. He crouched flat on his belly, his quivering tail beat the ground. Suddenly he leapt into the air and screamed. Even the elephant felt the few stiff hairs on his thick neck straighten, rigidly. Both animals and their witnesses were drowned in a flood of falling leaves.

Sadly but admiringly, the elephant said to the tiger: "Your roar is indeed without equal, my friend. I will lie down and offer you my life. But please, let me have one more day to live for I want to visit my family back home. The day after tomorrow, at noon, you will find me here waiting for you." The triumphant tiger generously accepted this demand. His mind was already occupied with the battle he was going to wage against the lord of the jungle, the awesome lion.

Walking home, the elephant was very depressed. "Very soon," he thought to himself, "I will no longer be walking like this, feeling the solid earth give under my feet or squirting my friends in the mudhole. And all those ripe bananas! Those nasty monkeys will peel them and eat them without even a thought for me who will no longer be there." The elephant's eyes welled up with tears.

"Uncle Elephant, why in heaven are you looking so sad?"

The elephant looked around but saw no one. "Here I am, right here." It was the friendly hare, a tiny, mischievous, but good-hearted fellow.

"Sad!" the elephant grunted in a mournful voice. "I am going to die the day after tomorrow, Nephew Hare."

"You? Die? What are you talking about?" the hare exclaimed, his ears pricking up, rigid like two iris blades. The elephant sat down on his hind legs and began to tell his friend about all that had happened.

"Oh, don't you think a minute of dying for that scoundrel the tiger!" The hare had never looked more determined. "I have an idea! If you want to live, I will try to save you!" But the elephant was not one to go back on his word. "No, no," he told the hare, "I have given the tiger my promise. I would rather die than cheat."

The two animals walked together in silence for a long moment. Suddenly, the small hare leapt up in joy. "All right! You are a gentleman and gentlemen keep promises. You will not have to do anything but lie down, as you told the tiger, and let me take care of the rest. Is that all right with you?"

Seeing that his life could be saved while keeping his word, the elephant accepted the proposition. He wondered, nonetheless, how in the world the tiny hare was going to save him.

Two days later, at noon, the friends found themselves at the contest place. The elephant lay down on the ground while the hare hid himself behind his massive bulk. Soon the tiger appeared, walking slowly, majestically toward them.

As soon as he saw the tiger, the hare jumped on top of the elephant and began hopping up and down. And while dancing he sang: "One elephant, I'll eat it up! Two elephants, I'll eat them up! Three elephants, I'll eat them up!" The tiger was approaching nearer and nearer but the hare went on dancing and singing. "One elephant, I'll eat it up! Two elephants, I'll eat them up..."

The strong but cautious tiger stopped dead in his tracks. "What's this?" he thought. "I have arrived too late. The hare has gotten here before me and thrown the elephant down. How strong he must be! One elephant, he'll eat it up! I doubt that I would be able to down even a quarter of it let alone one whole elephant or two or three!"

"Ah! ah! There is Uncle Tiger!" the hare called to him. "You are late! This big silly elephant was just standing around here. Would you imagine that? Had he not heard of me, The Great Hare of the Jungle? I threw him down so hard he died instantly. Do you think I don't like elephant meat as much as you do? But still, this is going to be a very poor dinner. Three elephants are just what I need to be satisfied!" Then, jumping off the elephant, the little animal started hopping toward the tiger: "But say, you came at the right moment! You will do as my dessert!"

Incredible as it is, the tiger took one step back, then two steps back, then turned around and ran for his life. . . .

The tiger ran and ran, through forests and across streams until he heard somebody shriek at him to stop. It was the clever monkey. Huffing and puffing, the tiger began to tell the monkey of his misadventure.

"Come now," the monkey declared haughtily, "it must have been something else! Don't tell me that you are afraid of a hare?"

"Yes, I am. I saw him with my own eyes! Dancing and

singing on top of the dead elephant! He sang that he would eat even two or three of them, not only one! He even wanted me for his dessert. He actually walked toward me, ready to pounce on me!"

"I don't believe a word of it!" the monkey maintained. "I want to see for myself. If the hare is still there, I will handle him while you take care of what might be left of the elephant. You must be hungry, aren't you?" He gave the tiger a mischievous look. Reluctantly, the tiger agreed.

In order to go faster, the tiger let the monkey jump on his back and hold him around the neck with his long arms. When they arrived at the place, the elephant was no longer there. Only the hare was seen, licking his lips and cleaning his whiskers with visible delight. As soon as the hare saw the two friends, he jumped up and patting his belly, yelled at them: "That was a pretty skinny elephant! I am still so hungry! But good little monkey! How thoughtful of you!" Hopping wildly, the hare looked the very picture of happiness. But suddenly he stopped dancing. "But what is that you brought me? Only one tiger? Don't you know you owe me three? Miserable cheat! Cheat! Cheat! You owe me three big tigers and you have brought me only a small one! I'll show you. . . ."

Before the hare had finished his invectives, the tiger understood. He realized that the monkey, with his arms wrapped tightly around his neck, had tricked him into coming here to be paid off as a debt. Turning around, he began a second run for his life.

The tiger ran so fast this time that the monkey did not dare jump off his back. He ran so hard that his body went through thick bushes as if they were spider webs. Finally, exhausted, he slumped down on the ground as though all his bones had been broken. Looking back, he was surprised and furious to see the monkey's head dangling over his shoulder, a big grin baring his sharp white teeth. But his anger evaporated quickly. The monkey, with his arms still tight around the tiger's neck, had simply died of fright. . . .

Now, more than ever, the tiger was convinced that the hare was a monstrous animal. He did not realize that the monkey had not died from fear of the hare, but because of the tiger's own terrible running.

No one knows why, but the tiger's mishaps were recounted throughout the land over and over again. When, at last, he realized that he had been tricked by the clever but gentle hare, he felt the terrible shame which has never left him. As it happens, the Viet-Namese word for "tiger" is "ho." Oddly enough, "ho" also means "shame" or "ashamed." Looking at the tiger, nobody would think he could be ashamed of anything. But he is, and the hare, better than anyone else, knows why.

THE TIGER'S STRIPES

◎◎◎◎◎

A long time ago, the tiger's coat was a source of great pride to him. In the shadows of the forest, under the moonlight, the great feline's body was an undulating and powerful mass of glittering gold.

But today, he loathes the irregular black stripes which mar his once perfect fur. To him, these beautiful stripes look like nothing but the marks of a cruel slashing whip. Nevertheless, he has learned to live with them. And ironically, these very marks have made him even more elusive. Lurking in the elephant grass or crouching behind a thicket, the tiger, blending into his surroundings, is all but invisible.

Let no one think for a moment, however, that when the tiger's coat was of a uniform golden brown he was any less fearsome. His reputation for swiftness and power, cruelty and greed was already established. It is well known that a lion who has just eaten never kills. The tiger, though, has always been ready for attack.

IT WAS such an animal which had been terrorizing the population of a whole mountain village. The people had been living peacefully in their day-to-day routine when suddenly fear erupted like a volcano. In less than a week the tiger had visited their hamlet three times. A calf, another calf, then a prize pig disappeared. The villagers were afraid and puzzled. The large beast—his footprints were enormous—was a particularly cunning, swift, and strong one. The raids had taken place noiselessly, because the dogs, usually vigilant, had kept quiet. The bamboo fences surrounding the houses had remained undisturbed.

Afraid of losing any of his cattle, one man angrily mounted guard himself and, with two other men, waited all night for the killer. Confronted by three men armed with spears and swords, the tiger beat a quick retreat, but not before he had swiftly and savagely struck one of the men. The victim died of a fractured skull. By now, the Tiger King, so named for his huge size, had become the most feared and hated creature in the whole valley. There, he reigned supreme.

For quite some time, the Tiger King had had his eye on a big black buffalo he saw almost every day, pulling the plow in the fields for its master. From behind the grass and bushes of the hill, high above the village, the Tiger King often gazed down at the working team. But as yet, the Tiger King wanted no battle with them. He thought, "If the big buffalo with his sharp horns seems so strong that I think twice before attacking it, how dangerous and powerful the man must be to remain its master!"

As the days passed the Tiger King became more and more impatient. Still, instead of going to the field and risking a bloody fight, he was cunning enough to remain hidden and wait for the right moment.

One morning the farmer came to his rice field as usual, but apparently having forgotten something, he disappeared after a moment, leaving his buffalo behind. From afar, the tiger watched all this. "I will go and try to make friends with the buffalo," the Tiger King thought suddenly, "and strike him when he least suspects it. Then I'll hide him in the bush," he thought again, on the way down to the field, "and when the man returns, I will handle him without his buffalo's help!"

Swiftly, the Tiger King approached the buffalo, trying to look as gentle as he could. "Listen, friend, I have come with no harmful intentions. I only want to ask you something which has been bothering me for some time."

Although frightened, the good buffalo remained calm. "Oh, it's you, friend Tiger! How nice to see you! What is this that I can do for you?"

"Well, friend Buffalo," the tiger said, maneuvering himself all the while into a good place from which to leap at the unsuspecting buffalo, "I have been admiring you for a long, long time now. Your strength! Your industry!" The tiger raised his eyes toward heaven. "How you can ever pull this heavy plow is beyond me. And the way you work! From dawn to dusk with but a short, short break at noon! I think you are wonderful, friend Buffalo, wonderful, admirable. . . ."

Despite his fear, the buffalo was pleased. Here was the Tiger King himself, standing in the mud of the field, praising *him,* the lowly plow-puller! But he did not relax his guard. Every time the tiger moved, he, too, moved. The Tiger King always found the huge, curved, sharp horns facing him.

"I think you are admirable," the Tiger King repeated. "If it were not for your master, the farmer—"

"What of my master, friend Tiger?" the buffalo inquired, somewhat taken aback.

"Well, now, don't take offense, friend Buffalo. I think you

have been letting yourself be unjustly exploited by that man. I don't know what he would do to pull this heavy plow without your help. But he treats you badly, very badly. Go! Stop! Left! Right! All those orders! And that bamboo cane in his hand. . . . He whips you every three steps you take! What a cruel, hard man! If I were in your place, I would . . ."

But the Tiger King was interrupted. The buffalo did not like to hear his beloved master abused.

"You are wrong, my dear friend," he said to the Tiger King. "The man is as good as he can be. He has to give orders so I will know where to go. And his whip is not meant to hurt me! My skin is too thick for that wisp of bamboo! Besides, he is kind and gives me food and shelter. And, of course, he is my master because he has intelligence."

"Intelligence!" interjected the Tiger King, edging closer. "What's that? I have never heard of it before. What does an intelligence look like?"

Shaking his head, the buffalo faced the tiger with his horns. "I don't know, I really don't! I have never seen it myself. But I know he has it because people talk about it. They say that that's why he is so powerful and clever. By the way, he will be back any moment now, and you could ask him about it yourself."

The Tiger King's curiosity was aflame. For once he was not as cautious as he should be. He decided to wait for the man's return.

As soon as the farmer rounded the corner of the path, he came face to face with the tiger. But having been taught what to do in such a situation, the man knew better than to turn on his heels and run.

"Master!" the buffalo called to him. "Here is my friend, Tiger. He asks to see your intelligence! Won't you please show it to him?"

The Tiger King chimed in: "Show it to me, Farmer! I want to see it, just for once. Is it true that it helps you to be clever and powerful? Why then haven't I got it?"

Completely recovered now from the initial shock, the farmer threw his hands up: "Well, well, good morning Mister Tiger, sir! Why in heaven didn't you come a bit earlier, before I went home to fetch my lunch? I certainly would have brought my intelligence back to show you. It's too big and too heavy to carry around you know! I always leave it at home."

The tiger was thoroughly disappointed. But his disappointment did not make him forget that the real reason he was there was to assault both buffalo and man. Now that he was seeing them at close quarters, they didn't look as big and dangerous as they had from afar. "Perhaps I could try to take them on right here and now," the Tiger King thought, and his tail began to quiver as it always did before an attack. . . . But quickly the farmer said to the tiger: "Oh, all right, all right! Don't look so miserable, sir! Since you came here all the way from the jungle, I don't want you to go back without having seen it. I'll return in a moment." Thereupon the farmer turned on his heel and started home. But before going a dozen feet, he re-traced his steps hurriedly and said to the tiger, "But look here! To oblige you I'm willing to go all the way home to get my intelligence. But I don't want to leave you alone here with my buffalo. Who would help me plow my fields if you ate up my buffalo?" The tiger protested vigorously that he had no intention of doing so, but the farmer was adamant and refused to leave.

Suddenly the man slapped his thigh triumphantly. "Well, if you want to see my intelligence so much, why don't you let me tie you up to this tree here? Then I wouldn't worry about my buffalo."

The Tiger King looked at the man, then at his buffalo, then back at the man, then back at his buffalo. More than ever, they seemed so mild, so humble to him. Now that his master was back, the buffalo was behaving in his usual docile, gentle way. He was standing there with his head slightly bent down, his eyes thoughtful and sad. "And the farmer! That puny man!" thought the Tiger King. "I have to see this fellow's intelligence. I will take it from him and then I will kill and eat them both." Having made up his mind, the Tiger King agreed to the farmer's proposal.

Making the tiger stand upright against the trunk of a nearby tree, the man began to encircle the animal with yards of strong rope. No sooner was the final knot tied than the farmer quickly unfastened the heavy plow from his buffalo, and with all his strength started to beat the captive tiger who roared in pain and fury.

Finally, maddened to extraordinary strength, the Tiger King managed to get one of his hind feet against the tree and in one incredible push broke the strong binding rope. But instead of turning upon his intended victims, he ran desperately for his life.

The tiger has never looked the same since. Having struggled so hard to free himself, he forced the rope to sear his fur, burning dark lines all over his body.

Because he knows now what man's intelligence is, the tiger has become an even more treacherous and bitter enemy, an eternal "man-eater." Never again will he dare come down from his mountain lair in daylight to molest the domestic beasts or their masters. His marred fur is always there to remind him of man's cunning.

THAT FOURTH LEG
OF THE DOG

◎◎◎◎◎

LONG, long ago, the dog had only three legs. Left or right, nobody knows, but it was one of his hind legs that was missing. How he managed to move about, much less to run, is a matter of imagination. What is certain is that all the other animals had either two, four, or more legs. Only the poor dog had three.

Unlike today, rabbits used to come almost under the dog's nose and tease him mercilessly. Cats did not even bother to look at him. The last thing he could imagine was to try and catch those stray pheasants. The dog was ashamed, angry, miserable. So much so that one beautiful day, sitting by himself, he could no longer contain his feelings and burst out crying.

Rarely, if ever, have animal tears been so bitter. But suddenly the dog looked up, startled by strange soft music and a heavenly scent. The Lord Buddha, Himself, was standing before him. Under the Enlightened One's feet, a new white lotus flower shone pearly in the sun.

"My child," the Buddha said to the dog, "your tears are so heavy they shake the ground and move my heart. What is it that makes you so unhappy?"

Prostrating himself at the Lord's feet, the dog told him about his missing leg and begged for help. He knew that the Buddha was all-powerful, all-knowing, all-charity.

Smiling, the Buddha bent down, plucked a petal from the lotus flower, and placed it where the fourth leg would be, near the tail. The dog turned his head to look at the flower petal. But he did not see it. In its place was a leg he had never seen before. Leaping up with joy, the dog wanted to express his gratitude to his benefactor, but the Buddha had gone. All that remained was the distant music in the air and the fading lotus scent.

So happy was he, the dog stood motionless for a long moment. Then, suddenly, barking with joy, he began to run. He ran across meadows and fields, over hills and valleys. Transported by an indescribable gaiety, he ran and ran so fast his four legs barely touched the ground.

The dog stopped at last, completely exhausted. After such excitement and strenuous running he suddenly felt he had to relieve himself. There, near a big banyan tree, he stood. But the sight of the sacred tree reminded him that it was the Buddha who had given him his fourth leg. Full of gratitude for this precious, miraculous gift, the good dog delicately raised it high in the air. . . .

That is why, today, one always sees dogs acting in such a dainty fashion.

But the dog's precious leg and his good manners toward it have, unfortunately, given rise to another tragedy of sorts.

As everyone knows, Buddhist monks are highly spiritual men, vegetarians by taste and discipline. They do not even touch those vegetables which are considered harmful to the purity of one's mind and body, such as onion and garlic.

Once, at a certain pagoda, there lived a young novice who was working and studying to become a full-fledged monk. This young novice had been struggling mightily against his desire for more flavorful food. And as he came from a part of the country which considered dog meat to be one of the greatest delicacies on earth, he longed for a bit of it day and night. Day and night his thoughts were troubled by visions of slices of dog meat with plenty of garlic and soy sauce on them, broiling furiously over the red charcoal. Then, desperately, he gave up his fight. A few days later, a villager discovered that he had lost his beloved dog.

Somehow or other the villagers were convinced that the beast had been stolen, slaughtered, and eaten by the aspiring monk. The alleged culprit was brought to the village court. Poor young monk, he was all but shattered. Not only was he liable to serve a prison term for having stolen another's property, but also he suffered from the shame his crime had brought upon himself and his pagoda. Nonetheless, begging for mercy, he invoked attenuating circumstances.

"Attenuating what?" the village councilman interjected disdainfully. "You stole it, killed it, ate it, and you have confessed. But, young monk, even if we are readily willing to forgive you for your theft, since it was only a dog, we cannot pass over your other misdeeds. As a Buddhist novice, you should know better than to eat meat. You deceived the church and the people. That is most serious."

Silently the young novice bent his head. One could see beads of perspiration on his temple. But when he looked up, his voice was soft and tranquil. "No, sir, I have not committed that crime. My mind and body have not been stained with animal flesh."

"What do you mean? You have eaten the dog, have you not?" The village councilman was white with rage.

"Yes," the novice answered. "Yes, I have eaten it. But I have not eaten the whole dog, only one of the hind legs." Pausing, he then continued, "Is it not true, as you, sirs, all know, that the Buddha Himself in His compassion gave the dog this hind leg? It was made from a petal of the lotus, was it not? How can anyone imagine that the Lord Buddha, the Infinitely En-lightened One, could have given the dog a leg created from flesh which is sinful and impure? I have stolen and killed and deserve to remain in hell forever, but, please, do not accuse me of deceiving anyone by eating meat. What I ate was only a vegetable leg, a lotus petal, if I may say so."

THE
LiTTLE,
LiZARDS
SORROW

◎◎◎◎◎

There is in Viet-Nam a certain species of small lizard only three inches long with webbed feet and a short, round head. They are often seen indoors, running swiftly upside down on the ceiling or along the walls, emitting little snapping cries that sound like "Tssst ... tssst!" Suppose that you drop an egg on the kitchen floor; the kind of sound you would make then, with the tip of your tongue between your teeth, is like the cry of these harmless, funny little lizards. Sounds of mild sorrow, of genuine shock but somehow humorous regret that seem to say, "Oh, if only I had been ... If only I had known ... Oh, what a pity, what a pity ... Tssst! Tssst!"

THERE was once a very rich man whose house was immense and filled with treasures. His land was so extensive that, as the Viet-Namese say, "Cranes fly over it with outstretched wings," for cranes only do so over very long distances. Wealth breeding vanity, one of the rich man's greatest pleasures was beating other rich men at a game he himself had invented. One player would announce one of his rare possessions, the other would counter the challenge by saying that he, too—if he really did— owned such a treasure. "A stable of fifty buffalos," one man would say. The other would reply, "Yes, I also have fifty of them." It was then his turn to announce, "I sleep in an all-teak bed encrusted with mother-of-pearl." The first player would lose if he slept on cherry planks!

One day, a stranger came to the rich man's house. Judging from his appearance, the gatekeeper did not doubt that the visitor was a madman. He wanted, he said, to play the famous game with the mansion's master. Yet dressed in clothes that looked as if they had been mended hundreds of times, and wearing broken straw sandals, the stranger appeared to be anything but a wealthy man. Moreover, his face was gaunt and pale as if he had not had a good meal in days. But there was such proud, quiet dignity to the stranger that the servant did not dare shut the gates in his face. Instead, he meekly went to inform his master of the unlikely visitor's presence. Intrigued, the man ordered that the pauper be ushered in.

Trying to conceal his curiosity and surprise, the rich man offered his visitor the very best chair and served him hot, perfumed tea.

"Well, stranger, is it true that you have deigned to come here to play a game of riches with me?" he began inquiringly.

The visitor was apparently unimpressed by the rich surroundings, giving them only a passing, casual look. Perfectly at ease, sipping his tea from the rare porcelain cup, he answered in a quiet though self-assured voice, "Yes, sir, that is if you, too, so wish."

"Naturally, naturally," the rich man raised his hand in a sweeping motion. "But, may I ask, with your permission, where you reside and what is your honorable occupation?"

The stranger gave a little chortle, visibly amused. "Sir, would you gain any to know about these? I came here simply to play your game; only, I have two conditions, if you are so generous as to allow them."

"By all means! Pray, tell me what they are," the rich man readily inquired.

The visitor sat farther back on the brocaded chair, his voice soft and confidential. "Well, here they are. A game is no fun if the winner does not win anything and the loser does not lose anything. Therefore I would suggest that if I win I would take everything in your possession—your lands, your stables, your servants, your house and everything contained in it. But if you win—" Here the stranger paused, his eyes narrowed ever so slightly, full of humorous malice, "If you win, you would become the owner of everything that belongs to me." The stranger paused again. "And what belongs to me, sir, you will have no idea of. I am one of the most fortunate men alive, sir. . . . And besides that," he added with a knowing look, "I would remain in this house to serve you as a domestic the rest of my life."

For a long moment, the rich man sat back in silence. Another long moment went by, then the rich man spoke: "That's agreed. But, please tell me your other condition."

Eyes dreamy, the stranger looked out of the window. "My second condition, sir, is not so much a condition as a request. I hope you would not mind giving me, a visitor, an edge over you. May I be allowed to ask the first question?"

The rich man thought for a long second, then said, "That is also agreed. Let's begin."

"Do I really understand that you have agreed to both my conditions?" the stranger asked thoughtfully.

Something in the visitor's manner and voice hurt the rich man's pride. He was ready to stake his very life on this game that he himself had created. There was no way out. "Yes," he said. "Yes, indeed I have. Now tell me, please, what do you have that I have not got?" The stranger smiled. Reaching to his feet, he took up his traveling bag, a coarse cotton square tied together by the four ends. Opening it slowly, ceremoniously, he took out an object and handed it to his host without a word. It was an empty half of a coconut shell, old and chipped, the kind poor people use as a container to drink water from.

"A coconut-shell cup!" the rich man exclaimed. One could not know whether he was merely amused or completely shattered.

"Yes, sir, a coconut-shell cup. A *chipped* shell cup. I use it to drink from on my wanderings. I am a wanderer," the visitor said quietly.

Holding the shell between his thumb and his forefinger and looking as if he had never seen such an object before, the rich man interrupted, "But, but you don't mean that I do not have a thing like this?"

"No, sir, you have not. How could you?" the stranger replied.

Turning the residence upside down, the man and his servants discovered odds and ends of one thousand and one kinds, but they were unable to produce a drinking cup made from a coconut shell. In the servants' quarters, however, they found a few such utensils, but they were all brand new, not chipped. One could imagine that the servants of such a wealthy man would not deign to drink from a chipped cup. Even a beggar would throw it away. . . .

"You see, sir," the stranger said to the rich man once they were again seated across the tea table, "you see, I am a wanderer, as I have said. I am a free man. This cup here is several years old and my only possession besides these poor clothes I have on. If you do not think me too immodest, I would venture that I treasure it more than you do all your collections of fine china. But, from this day, I am the owner and lone master of all that belongs to you...."

Having taken possession of the rich man's land, houses, herds and all his other treasures, the stranger began to give them away to the poor and needy people. Then, one day, taking up his old cotton bag, he left the village and no one ever saw him again.

As for the dispossessed rich man, it is believed that he died of grief and regret and was transformed into this small lizard. Curiously, one sees him scurrying about only indoors. Running up and down the walls, crossing the ceiling, staring at people and furniture, he never stops his "Tssst, Tssst." Viet-Namese children, in particular, are very fond of him for he looks so harassed, so funny.

But, oh, such sorrow, such regret, such self-pity.

THE
SAND-CARRIER
CRAB

◎◎◎◎◎

DA-TRANG was a young hunter from Son-Tay province, in the northernmost part of Viet-Nam. His was a simple and peaceful life. With bow and arrows he left home every morning at dawn for the forest where game was plentiful. Da-Trang was very clever with his bow and had sharp ears and eyes. A few rabbits and pheasants, and now and then a small deer or mountain goat, were sufficient to help him support his family.

One day, on his way home from the forest, Da-Trang witnessed a hair-raising scene. An unusually large, yellow snake was fighting against two small black ones. In awe, the hunter stood watching. With lightning speed, the reptiles darted forward and backward, raised themselves almost vertically from the ground, then lay flattened upon it, their yellow-and-black coils flashing. Suddenly, one of the black snakes reared its head in agony and fell back abruptly like a broken stick. The other black snake began to flee but it was immediately pursued by its yellow adversary. Without hesitation, Da-Trang ran after them. Instinctively, he raised his bow. An arrow hissed and struck the large reptile, fastening it to the ground.

Retracing his steps, the hunter came upon the body of the dead black snake. It was a female, Da-Trang's trained eyes told him. Even though he had killed many animals, his heart was filled with pity at the sight of the reptile that died without her mate. Out of sympathy, Da-Trang dug a hole with his large machete and buried her.

That very night, Da-Trang dreamed of a black-clad, white-haired old man who came to thank him for having saved his life and buried his wife's body. When Da-Trang expressed surprise, the visitor told him that he was the genie of that part of the forest and that he was strolling with his wife, in the form of snakes, when they were attacked by the monster.

Then the old man handed him what felt like a small egg. "Please accept this as a token of my gratitude," he said. "Hold it in your mouth and you will be able to hear and understand the languages of all birds and beasts." When the last words were spoken, the genie opened his mouth, wide and red. Da-Trang was horrified, seeing it was not the mouth of a human being but that of a snake. He shuddered and woke suddenly. Near his hand, in the blackness, the gleam of a round object gave the room an eerie light.

Da-Trang found himself the proud owner of a snake-pearl. It was no larger than a pigeon egg, but holding it in his mouth, Da-Trang could indeed understand what were only animal noises for others. This ability gave him more joy and pleasure than he could ever have imagined. Walking in the forest, he felt he was the center of the world, the bridge on which the universe of man meets that of insects, birds, beasts, and fish. He could hear the faintest rustle in the leaves and follow a conversation between chipmunks. He heard the chip-chip of sparrows and worried about the fate of frightened worms he had just passed by.

One day, a crow called to him: "Da-Trang! Da-Trang! A deer is over there! A deer is over there!" Guided by the bird, he spotted a lone deer standing in the shade of a cypress. When he had killed it, he left the animal's entrails on a branch for his helper. A working relationship thus developed between crow and man: the former flew around looking for game, the latter shot it and fed his guide.

But the friendship did not last long, for one day, another beast apparently stole the crow's reward. Furious and spiteful, he accused Da-Trang of cheating. A heated argument ensued, and unable to restrain his anger at being insulted by a miserable blackbird, Da-Trang raised his bow toward it. But this one time, his arrow missed its target, and the crow flew after it and caught it with his claws. Flying away, he shrieked at his old friend: "You will pay for it! Da-Trang! You will pay for it!"

Some time afterward, sudden misfortune came, shattering the hunter's peace and happiness. Chained and yoked, he was led to prison by soldiers who told him that a man's corpse had been found floating down the river with an arrow through its chest bearing his name. The crow had kept his vow of vengeance. It must have been easy for him, once he saw the drowned body of a man, to plant the arrow in it. Despite Da-Trang's protests, nobody believed his tale. He was condemned to a dungeon for the rest of his life.

Alone in his stone cell, Da-Trang spent mournful days staring at a tiny hole far up near the ceiling where a little light came pouring in. When the light was bright and golden, he knew it was sunny outside; when it was gray and pale, he knew evening was falling. This light was all that remained with him of those carefree days he had spent hunting in the forest. And although he had succeeded, by clever ruses, in keeping the pearl with him, Da-Trang was unable to use it. Now and then he would hear some distant birds chirping, but he could not make out their conversation.

Then one evening, when the cell was quite black with

shadows and Da-Trang was about to fall asleep, some soft mur-
muring startled him. It was the tiny black ants on the wall of
the cell. Da-Trang listened. A flood, a terrible flood was coming,
they said to each other excitedly.

The next time Da-Trang saw his jailer, he passed on the
news without revealing its source. But the man only laughed.
The country, he said, had been going through the worst
drought in a decade; not a single cloud could be seen on the
horizon. The big flood, however, did arrive, carrying away
hundreds of houses and drowning thousands of people and
animals.

Another day, Da-Trang heard a couple of sparrows chattering
away, standing at the little hole of his cell. His heart leapt
with joy. Their chirps were far more than mere gossip. This
time the prisoner boldly asked to be taken to the province's
governor himself. As his prophecy was now taken more seri-
ously, thanks to the flood, his request was promptly granted.

Face to face with the official, Da-Trang revealed what the
sparrows had told him. For the last few years, the province's
granary had been short of its quota and the price of rice had
risen drastically. This was not due, however, to birds and mice,
as the officer who guarded the granary pretended. He, himself,
was guilty of stealing a tremendous quantity of it. Testing
Da-Trang's statement, the governor ordered a thorough investi-
gation. Da-Trang was proven right and the granary officer was
sent to forced labor. From then on, although remaining in his
cell, Da-Trang enjoyed little privileges and a great deal of
respect from his once-brutish guards.

Da-Trang's fame began to spread far and wide. His Majesty,
the Emperor himself, heard of him and one day the prisoner,

now a gray-haired man, was summoned to the court. At the Emperor's request, Da-Trang humbly related his whole story: how he saved the black snake, how the snake gave him the magic pearl, about the crow and its vengeance, about the ants and the birds whose conversations he understood.

Da-Trang's listeners were thrilled and awed by his extraordinary tale. Then and there, the Emperor ordered that he be relieved of his unjust imprisonment. Furthermore, his wife and children were sent for and together the Da-Trang family was kept at the court and granted a life of comfort and riches.

Now a free and famous man, Da-Trang often accompanied his ruler on the latter's wanderings among the animals. Having grown tired of his human subjects' arguments and gossip, the Emperor frequently borrowed Da-Trang's magic pearl and delighted in listening to the animals and birds. This, however, lasted only a short time. His Majesty soon discovered that he became as weary of the chatter among animals as he had been of that among men. Eager to please his protector, one day Da-Trang suggested that they go to the sea where the creatures' voices might be more enchanting. So they went east, ruler and subject, to the end of the land, toward the sea. But again, the Emperor grew tired of listening. Fish and shrimps, clams and oysters had no more imagination, His Majesty declared, than land beasts and human beings.

One day, just before their departure back to the capital, Da-Trang spotted a small squid swimming near their boat and drew the Emperor's attention to it. The monarch put the magic pearl in his mouth and listened to its singing. The small, dark creature sang of the beauty of the ocean, the sky and the clouds. He sang that life was short and that he was the king of his own heart. He sang of his prized solitude and his care-free wandering.

The Emperor listened to the squid's singing, fascinated. When the song ended, the squid dipped his body three times in sign of homage and farewell, and disappeared. Bending over the boat's side, transported by the song's noble beauty, the Emperor uttered a cry of satisfaction. Da-Trang's hand shot out but it was too late. From the Emperor's mouth, the precious pearl fell into the sea and disappeared.

Da-Trang was inconsolable. By then, the pearl had become the center of his being. It had helped him find game, delivered him from life imprisonment, brought him honor and riches. Now it was lost. Slowly, the former hunter grew mad with sorrow.

Completely out of his senses, Da-Trang conceived the idea of filling up the sea in order to find his beloved pearl. He was convinced that by pouring sand into the bay he could raise the sea's bottom so that one day the pearl would surface on top of the sand. And since it was he who had lost the pearl, the Emperor had the incredible project carried out. Thousands upon thousands of sand carts were pushed to the shore and emptied into the ocean.

But soon the Emperor grew exasperated at seeing so much labor wasted on the hopeless undertaking. Da-Trang found himself all alone in his work. Every day, and often at night, he was seen carting sand to the seashore and emptying it into the ocean. He grieved and worked, worked and grieved, to the last day of his life. . . .

It is believed that after his death, Da-Trang's soul took the shape of one of those innumerable little gray crabs which are seen on most Viet-Namese beaches. Darting swiftly here and there, the tiny crabs work all day long rolling little balls of sand with their claws and feet. But as soon as these balls are gathered into a pile, a new wave arrives and licks them all away. With incredible speed, the little crabs begin their work again. A new pile of sand balls is gathered. A new wave roars in, its tongue again smoothing down the sandy stretch.

Dã Tràng xe cát biển đông,
Nhọc lòng mà chẳng nên công cán gì.

The Viet-Namese say this when they see someone carrying on an absurd and hopeless task. Literally, the proverb means:

"Pushing the sand cart, Da-Trang tries to fill
up the Eastern Sea,
His heart and his body are weary, but no
progress is ever made."

◎◎◎◎◎

EVERYONE in the village knew the usurer, a rich and smart man. Having accumulated a fortune over the years, he settled down to a life of leisure in his big house surrounded by an immense garden and guarded by a pack of ferocious dogs. But still unsatisfied with what he had acquired, the man went on making money by lending it to people all over the county at exorbitant rates. The usurer reigned supreme in the area, for numerous were those who were in debt to him.

One day, the rich man set out for the house of one of his peasants. Despite repeated reminders, the poor laborer just could not manage to pay off his long-standing debt. Working himself to a shadow, the peasant barely succeeded in making ends meet. The moneylender was therefore determined that if he could not get his money back this time, he would proceed to confiscate some of his debtor's most valuable belongings. But the rich man found no one at the peasant's house but a small boy of eight or nine playing alone in the dirt yard.

"Child, are your parents home?" the rich man asked.

"No, sir," the boy replied, then went on playing with his sticks and stones, paying no attention whatever to the man.

"Then, where are they?" the rich man asked, somewhat irritated, but the little boy went on playing and did not answer.

When the rich man repeated his query, the boy looked up and answered, with deliberate slowness, "Well, sir, my father has gone to cut living trees and plant dead ones and my mother is at the market place selling the wind and buying the moon."

"What? What in heaven are you talking about?" the rich man commanded. "Quick, tell me where they are, or you will see what this stick can do to you!" The bamboo walking stick in the big man's hand looked indeed menacing.

After repeated questioning, however, the boy only gave the same reply. Exasperated, the rich man told him, "All right, little devil, listen to me! I came here today to take the money your parents owe me. But if you tell me where they really are and what they are doing, I will forget all about the debt. Is that clear to you?"

"Oh, sir, why are you joking with a poor little boy? Do you expect me to believe what you are saying?" For the first time the boy looked interested.

"Well, there is heaven and there is earth to witness my promise," the rich man said, pointing up to the sky and down to the ground.

But the boy only laughed. "Sir, heaven and earth cannot talk and therefore cannot testify. I want some living thing to be our witness."

Catching sight of a fly alighting on a bamboo pole nearby, and laughing inside because he was fooling the boy, the rich man proposed, "There is a fly. He can be our witness. Now, hurry and tell me what you mean when you say that your father is out cutting living trees and planting dead ones, while your mother is at the market selling the wind and buying the moon."

Looking at the fly on the pole, the boy said, "A fly is a good enough witness for me. Well, here it is, sir. My father has simply gone to cut down bamboos and make a fence with them for a man near the river. And my mother ... oh, sir, you'll keep your promise, won't you? You will free my parents of all their debts? You really mean it?"

"Yes, yes, I do solemnly swear in front of this fly here." The rich man urged the boy to go on.

"Well, my mother, she has gone to the market to sell fans so she can buy oil for our lamps. Isn't that what you would call selling the wind to buy the moon?"

Shaking his head, the rich man had to admit inwardly that the boy was a clever one. However, he thought, the little genius still had much to learn, believing as he did that a fly could be a witness for anybody. Bidding the boy good-by, the man told him that he would soon return to make good his promise.

A few days had passed when the moneylender returned. This time he found the poor peasant couple at home, for it was late in the evening. A nasty scene ensued, the rich man claiming his money and the poor peasant apologizing and begging for another delay. Their argument awakened the little boy who ran to his father and told him, "Father, father, you don't have to pay your debt. This gentleman here has promised me that he would forget all about the money you owe him."

"Nonsense," the rich man shook his walking stick at both father and son. "Nonsense, are you going to stand there and listen to a child's inventions? I never spoke a word to this boy. Now, tell me, are you going to pay or are you not?"

The whole affair ended by being brought before the mandarin who governed the county. Not knowing what to believe, all the poor peasant and his wife could do was to bring their son with them when they went to court. The little boy's insistence about the rich man's promise was their only encouragement.

The mandarin began by asking the boy to relate exactly what had happened between himself and the moneylender. Happily, the boy hastened to tell about the explanations he gave the rich man in exchange for the debt.

"Well," the mandarin said to the boy, "if this man here has indeed made such a promise, we have only your word for it. How do we know that you have not invented the whole story yourself? In a case such as this, you need a witness to confirm it, and you have none." The boy remained calm and declared that naturally there was a witness to their conversation.

"Who is that, child?" the mandarin asked.

"A fly, Your Honor."

"A fly? What do you mean, a fly? Watch out, young man, fantasies are not to be tolerated in this place!" The mandarin's benevolent face suddenly became stern.

"Yes, Your Honor, a fly. A fly which was alighting on this gentleman's nose!" The boy leapt from his seat.

"Insolent little devil, that's a pack of lies!" The rich man roared indignantly, his face like a ripe tomato. The fly was *not* on my nose; *he was on the housepole . . .*" But he stopped dead. It was, however, too late.

The majestic mandarin himself could not help bursting out laughing. Then the audience burst out laughing. The boy's parents too, although timidly, laughed. And the boy, and the rich man himself, also laughed. With one hand on his stomach, the mandarin waved the other hand toward the rich man:

"Now, now, that's all settled. You have indeed made your promises, dear sir, to the child. *Housepole or no housepole, your conversation did happen after all!* The court says you must keep your promise."

And still chuckling, he dismissed all parties.

The Horse
and
The Eighteen Bandits

◉◉◉◉◉

Like most Far Eastern countries, Viet-Nam is dotted with temples, or pagodas. Although there is a Viet-Namese saying that "Buddha is in your heart," nothing can replace the sight of a Buddhist altar. Usually sitting or standing on a lotus blossom, the statue of the Lord occupies the central place in the temple.

Eternal peace and limitless charity—the Buddha's impassive yet smiling face conveys these to our hearts whether we are believers or not. To the left and right and behind the statue of the Lord are numerous statues of other *bodhisattvas,* or saints. All seem to express the same fundamental feelings reflected in the Buddha's face: peace and love. In a pagoda, one is never too far from perfection.

But to some people, especially foreign visitors, there is one puzzling, even disturbing note: the large number of strange, wooden or clay figures which flank the altar or stand behind it. These are the eighteen La-Hans, or Heavenly Beings. While differing in facial expression, they all look remarkably alike: all are muscular men wearing monks' robes; all have their heads close-shaven; and in varying degrees all their faces are monstrously ugly. Here is carved, into eighteen masks, whatever makes hell in men's lives. Some of them express, in a terrifying manner, gluttony and greed. Others, selfishness, envy. And others cruelty, brutality.

In the penumbra of the sacred hall, behind the serene, saintly faces, the eighteen La-Hans are all the more frightening. Nonetheless, in front of each of them stands an urn bristling with

incense sticks: the faithful worship them as they worship the
Lord Buddha Himself. No stranger would guess that before
they became La-Hans, these eighteen had been the most loathed
among men: they had been bandits.

FOR MANY years they had terrorized a large area in Viet-
Nam. Enormously strong, resourceful, cunning men, they always succeeded in eluding the soldiers sent out to capture them.
Over and over, tales of their cruelty and greed were told. They
rarely hesitated to kill the villagers and burn their houses whole
streets at a time after having stolen the possessions. It was said
that at only mention of the eighteen bandits, "The babes dared
not cry, the dogs dared not bark." Such was their evil fame.

One moonless night the bandits decided to attack a certain
rich man's house. But instead of encircling the house as they
usually did and storming it at a given signal, they stopped dead
at the darkened gate. The main hall of the large house was all
alight, and from within a cheerful voice called out to them:
"Please, do come in, gentlemen, please come in!" And out
walked the master of the house himself. The bandits grasped
their sword handles. One thought flashed through their minds
—strike down the man! But they held back; their curiosity was
aroused. Here they were, infamous murders, and yet the man
seemed as happy to see them as if they were his dearest friends.
He was even inviting them into his house for a late evening
repast. And in they went, taking care to keep the host in the
center of the group.

"If this turns out to be a treacherous idea of yours, you know
what we will do first!" the leader of the band said to the men,

who, looking at the eighteen naked swords around him, fully understood.

After having the man taste all the food and wine to make sure it had not been poisoned, the outlaws ate and drank and drank and ate. And while they did, the master of the house told why he had offered them this puzzling hospitality:

For many years, the man said, he had been the proud owner of a beautiful and fast horse. There was such understanding and friendship between master and beast that, excluding his wife and children, the man loved his horse more than he did anyone or anything.

Just the day before, during a ride, the horse started talking to his master. The latter couldn't believe his ears at first, he was so flabbergasted. But true enough, his horse was talking to him. It told him that on the next night, the eighteen bandits would descend upon his house. There was only one chance in a thousand that his house would not be burned to the ground and he not slain in the most atrocious manner. The only way to avert this disaster was to have a meal ready at a certain time with plenty of meat and wine, and for the master to come out at a given moment to greet his uninvited guests.

The leader of the band pointed the tip of his naked sword at the man's throat: "So, that's your story, eh! And you would like me to believe it, eh?! Well, let's go down to the stable and see what a horse's voice is like! After that, we will see how hard your neck is, compared to this lovely blade."

Preceded by the man, the eighteen bandits merrily made their way to the stable. There were several horses poking their heads out from the dark openings. "This one here, sirs, the white one here." The man pointed to his favorite.

Tall and graceful, with a long, flowing mane and thoughtful, almost human eyes, the white horse was an exceedingly beautiful animal, just as his master had said. And he talked! The bandits stepped back in astonishment, almost in fright.

"Yes, it is I who have told my master about your visit," the horse said in a clear, resounding voice. "Until today I have served him well. But unless I could do more for my master than just carry him on my back, I could never repay what I owe him."

In the hushed quiet of the night, his head bathed in the red glow of the flickering torches, the horse continued, "The Lord Buddha teaches that we all must live many lives. Each time a living thing is born, it carries in itself the reason for the preceding life. When a good man dies, his soul will come back to life in the form of another newborn whose destiny will be happiness and contentment. And a life of misery and suffering is the lot of someone whose earlier life was filled with misdeeds.

"I, myself, in my earlier life, was a man of this village, and my master here—" the horse looked at the host whose eyes were now red with tears— "and my master here did innumerable good things for me. He cared for me when I was ill, gave me and my family food when we were hungry. But I was an ungrateful man. When I became well and rich, I forgot my benefactor. Worse than that, I cheated him. When death came I still owed him a large sum of money."

The master of the horse looked about him in wonderment. Although still tightly grasping the handles of their swords, the eighteen outlaws remained silent; and the cruel, gleeful glint in their eyes had disappeared.

"But fortunately," the beautiful white horse continued, "fortunately, on the long way down to purgatory, I had time to reflect on and to regret my shameful conduct. Was it because of the deep sincerity of my repentance, or was it because of the mildness of my bad acts? I only know that instead of burning in hell's fire, I was ordered to return to life in the form of a horse, just as you see me now. I was to serve, and I do, this man here, to carry him on my back hour after hour, to go and to stop as he pleased. I was to let him kick me in the ribs and to whip me with his bamboo cane. I was to serve, to obey, to humble myself...and perhaps when I die, I will be allowed to return to life as another worthy human being...."

The horse spoke with such naturalness, such tranquility that all of the men forgot they were standing there in the dead of night, listening to an animal. "So, you know now who or what I am," the horse continued, steam from his nostrils whitening in the chilly mist. "Thus I have been serving my master to the utmost of my ability, in hopes of making up for my previous treachery. And, instead of treating me as an animal, as a slave, this man here loves me as a child, as a friend. Instead of insulting me, he talks to me; instead of kicking me, he encourages me, and instead of whipping me, he pats me.

"I believe that because of my sincere repentance and my master's unfailing kindness, I have been at last delivered from my damnation. I must, however, remain in the form of a horse until death, although my soul has been cleansed, my faults forgiven. And that is how, as a pure spirit, I was permitted by the Lord Buddha to know about your coming today to rob and murder my master. And, sirs, do you know that the voice with which I am talking to you now is not my own? It is the voice of the Lord, Himself....Please, spare my benefactor. Please, return to an honest life. The eighteen of you have killed, burned, robbed, lied enough for a thousand lives of burning in hell. Destroy your weapons before it is forever too late...."

That night, for the first time, the bandits returned from a raid without blood on their hands and gold in their bags. Since all of them had heard the horse talking, there was no possibility they had dreamed it. A strange tremor kept rising in their hearts. They thought about what the horse had said. Slowly, ever so slowly, their disbelief and wonderment turned to fear. And fearful, they began to know shame. If a man had been condemned to be a horse just because of his ungratefulness and dishonesty, what was to become of them, the eighteen blood-thirsty bandits? If their fear was bottomless, their shame was shattering. They walked back and forth in the secret cave and thought of the words of the horse. For several days, the eighteen bandits did not go down from their mountain hideout.

One day, the elderly headmonk of a large pagoda was visited by eighteen muscular strangers. The men said they desired to remain there to follow the Buddha's teachings. They had even shaven their heads in advance, so certain were they to be ac-cepted into the ranks of the ascetics. When the venerable head-monk inquired about this, he was told the truth: since for most of their lives they had been murderers and robbers of the most horrible kind, the bandits had doubted they would be forgiven even if they repented for the rest of their days. They had de-cided, finally, to ask the Lord Buddha himself. So one evening the eighteen bandits put all of their eighteen swords into a huge clay pot filled with water. Each then pricked his finger and let a few drops of his own blood fall into the pot. All night, they cooked the mixture over a large fire, at the entrance to their secret mountain cave.

When morning came, the bandits opened the big pot. The eighteen murderous blades had miraculously dissolved. They then understood that if a few drops of their own blood could destroy steel swords, their repentance was not too late for the all-loving, all-forgiving heart of the Lord Buddha.

At the temple, the former outlaws studied and fasted, prayed and meditated with such unrelenting fervor and total concentration that soon after their admittance, they were accepted as full-fledged monks. They lived to be very old men and their new lives were a long tale of selflessness. They would go through fire to save even an animal in danger. They would carry in their own arms a man stricken with plague. Finally, when they had gone past the stage of heroic deeds, they reached the time of enlightenment. The eighteen bandits became La-Hans, the Heavenly Beings.

Their statues now stand in the same chamber as the altar of the Buddha and the saints. To this day the former bandits are still depicted as the big, muscular men they once were. And though their hearts have been cleansed of all evil thoughts and all evil deeds, their monstrous faces remain unchanged.

Why? Is it because, despite all His Power, the Buddha could not change their ugly features? Or are the faces there to remind the people of what the eighteen La-Hans were before they met the horse? No one knows.

THE CROW'S PEARL

◎◎◎◎◎

THERE was once a buffalo-boy whose name was Qua which means crow. One would think that because of his name, Qua would have some special fondness for the noisy blackbirds. In truth, he loathed them. Being a buffalo-boy, he saw and heard them every day in the fields, and so was more than tired of their chatter.

One day, a terrible misfortune befell Qua. He lost his buffalo. The afternoon had been hot and Qua fell asleep while sitting with his back against the banyan tree. It was just a quick doze, but when he opened his eyes, the fat, black buffalo in his charge was gone.

Poor Qua spent hours looking for it but to no avail. The more frantic his search became, the less his mind dwelled on the lost buffalo and the more he began to imagine the punishments which would be heaped upon him, when he told the buffalo's owner what had happened. Just thinking of the owner's red face made Qua shiver all over like a rice leaf in the hot breeze. He no longer walked, he ran. He ran across the fields, through the bushes, over the hills, shouting his buffalo's name.

As the sun was beginning to set over the bamboo groves, Qua reached the point of exhaustion. He fell on his knees and, face in hands, cried his soul out. He cried and cried until tears no longer came. Then he just lay there on the grass, eyes open, knowing he was *not* going back to his master's; he would rather die.

For a long time Qua lay there, looking as if he were dead.

In fact he seemed so much so that several crows began to gather around him. One was even bold enough to saunter nearer and nearer to Qua's face. This bird was just going to poke his sharp beak into him, when Qua's hand flew out like lightning. His fingers tightened around the crow's neck.

"Aha!" the buffalo-boy exclaimed. "I caught you, you little black devil. I am not dead yet, you know! Now, I'm going to pluck off all your dirty feathers and then twist your neck. How do you like that?"

The crow went limp in the boy's hand. "No, no, sir, please, please don't! Please let me go and I will give you something precious you've never seen before in your whole life."

"You give me something?" Qua snorted. "Everybody knows that crows are liars! Now first your wing feathers..." and he began to pull on one.

The crow was desperate. "Oh, sir, please don't! I'll give you my pearl," it shrieked. And opening its beak widely the black-bird let fall out a glittering stone.

Qua grasped the pearl with his free hand. "That's a pretty bit of gravel! But what do you want me to do with it?" he asked his captive.

The crow hastened to explain. "Oh, sir, once I happened to free an earthworm and in recompense for my goodness, the Lord Buddha Himself gave that pearl to me saying that one day it would save my own life. The man who would not harm me, would only have to make a wish and immediately it would be fulfilled!"

"Well, well, that remains to be seen. If that's not true, you know what will happen to you," the buffalo-boy said and made his first wish aloud. Right then and there, standing before him, grazing peacefully, was the fat black buffalo Qua thought he had lost forever. The crow could not help thinking that the boy didn't have much imagination in wasting a whole wish on just a miserable buffalo—but although unimaginative, Qua kept his word. He tossed the crow into the air and the bird fluttered away, shrieking with happiness.

After returning the buffalo to its irate owner, Qua took the road of liberty. Standing on top of the first hill, the former buffalo-boy happily and loudly made his second wish....

Suddenly he found himself on the steps of an immense, beautiful brick house. There he made his third wish. In front of him, stretching out to the horizon were lush rice paddies dotted with busy field hands. Qua was now a rich man himself with house, land, servants, and cattle. Many years passed happily.

But one day, when Qua had reached manhood, he took the crow's pearl out and made yet another wish. Soon after, he met a nice girl of the village and married her, and was more than ever a happy man.

Qua's bliss, however, did not last long. One day he discovered that both his wife and his pearl had disappeared. This was more than he could bear, and Qua went back to the hilltop where he broke down crying as he had years ago when only a young, frightened buffalo-boy. He had been crying for some time and was almost asleep when a hand touched his shoulder, startling him. Wakening abruptly, half-blinded by a Golden Light, he realized it was the Lord Buddha Himself. Bending over the dazed Qua, the Buddha gave him two beautiful large flowers.

He said to Qua, "My child, here are two roses, one red, one white, and this is what you must do to have your pearl back."

Keeping the Buddha's instructions well in mind, Qua left the red rose at his own house and then set out for his parents-in-law's house with the white one. Since he had taken great care not to be noticed by anyone (just as the Buddha had instructed him), Qua reached his destination after dark. Stealthily he pinned the beautiful white rose on the entrance door of his in-laws' house. Then he left in a hurry. Two days later, as the Lord Buddha had instructed him, Qua returned to the house and asked to see his wife and her parents. What had happened meantime was beyond anyone's imagination.

The parents and their daughter were in a most horrible condition. On that morning when Qua's wife had found the beautiful white rose pinned at the entrance door, she had been overwhelmed by its fragrance. It was the most heavenly rose scent she had ever smelled. She sniffed the flower, and sniffed and sniffed until she was drunk from it. She called to her parents and they ran out and smelled the beautiful white rose. And then and there all their noses became longer and longer until, to each other's horror, each one had a nose as long as an elephant's trunk. For two days now the three of them had been wailing, crying, pulling out hair and holding their dangling noses in despair.

Now in their great misfortune, they did not even think of shutting the door in Qua's face. Instead they cried for his help, since he was the only person besides their servants who had seen them this way.

Qua, who understood everything, burst out laughing. He looked at his wife and told her to give the pearl back to him. When she tried to deny she had taken it, he rose from his chair. "All right then," he said. "You and your parents can keep the pearl, and your long noses as well, for I see that you must want them very much." Then he started toward the door.

"Oh, no! Please! You can't go away," wailed Qua's wife. "Please help us. I know that I have been an unworthy wife to you. I did steal the pearl and my parents and myself are being punished for my act. Please help us! I know that with the pearl you can make our noses return to their normal shapes." Then she ran to get the pearl and gave it back to her husband. Once he had the pearl safely in hand, Qua unbuttoned his jacket, pulled out the red rose and made the three culprits smell its fragrance.

That day, Qua walked home in triumph. The pearl was back in his pocket, and his wife, with her old, pretty nose (for she was a very pretty young woman) was walking respectfully a few steps behind him. And his wife's greedy parents were left behind, joyful that their noses had been shortened to their normal lengths, and likely never to forget this lesson in honesty.

It is said that Qua and his wife lived happily together until they grew very old. Many children were born to them and many, many children were born to their children. The house was so big that the whole clan could live together under its roof, and the fields were so fertile they could all live from their crops.

Qua lived to be almost a hundred years old. One afternoon, while he was sitting in the garden enjoying the fresh air of early autumn, he saw a big, black crow approaching. Passing low overhead the crow shrieked down at him:

>Where is my pearl?
>Where is my pearl?
>It must be returned!
>It must be returned!

Repeating this several times in a raucous voice, the crow flew away.

That same night old Qua died. Soon after his wife joined him. And when their children opened the small velvet-covered chest which contained the crow's pearl, it was gone.

A CAT IS A CAT IS A CAT

◎◎◎◎◎

THERE was a man who had a cat, a female cat.

It was not any cat; it was an extraordinary cat. Her black, white, and burnished-gold fur was thick and shiny. Her proportion was that of a poem by Li-Po, the great Chinese poet of the eighth century. Her bearing defied that of Empress Yang, the proudest and most beautiful woman of the Tang dynasty. And her eyes, oh, her eyes—there is no word to describe them.

The man was crazy about his cat. Just by looking at the animal, no one failed to forgive her master's pride. No one knew from where or from whom the lucky man had acquired his treasure. In any case, after the cat's arrival at his home, the man spent several days trying to find a suitable name for her.

During the day, the man barely paid any attention to his work and his food. At night, he tossed about in his bed, unable to sleep. He thought and thought and thought. Each time he thought he had found the right name, it only lingered at the tip of his tongue for a second, then quickly slid down his throat. No name seemed beautiful enough for his clever, proud, lovely cat. Again, he thought and thought. Then bang! THE name practically jumped out of his mouth. HEAVEN! what else could it be?

The man was so delighted with the name Heaven that he decided, then and there, to invite his friends over for a good dinner, just to tell them Heaven's name.

"Well, what is it?" the proud man's best friend, a gray-haired thin man, asked him. "What have you chosen for her?" Others joined in like a chorus, "Yes, what is it, how do you call her? Please, tell us now!" The dinner was over; contentedly they all were sipping rice wine. The man had kept his guests in suspense throughout the meal.

"Heaven," he said, pronouncing the syllables the way a jeweler handles pearls.

"Heaven!" the guests exclaimed at once in shock and disbelief.

"But for heaven's sake, why Heaven?" Again the thin man spoke first.

"Aha," said the host, pausing to enjoy his friends' expectant faces. "Well, heaven's the best, the top. The very best, the very top! What is, please tell me, better than heaven?" A shocked silence ensued. The guests could not believe that their wise and upright friend could be so blasphemous, vain, utterly ridiculous a man.

The thin man began to scratch his chin and everyone looked at him. He had always been the cleverest. At last, with his dreamy eyes fixed on the bamboo ceiling and addressing no one in particular, he mused aloud: "Hm-m, Heaven, Heaven...But a cloud! Yes, a cloud can darken heaven. A cloud can hide heaven's face!"

Hearing the word "cloud," the host's face indeed clouded over. "Cloud," he said, looking at his best friend whose mind had by then wandered into the nine clouds of deep meditation. "Cloud," he repeated. His eyes were at once melancholy and thoughtful. Then, it came like a flash. "I will call my cat Cloud then!" The gathering broke into hearty applause. The host's smile broadened into a huge grin. Another round of wine was poured.

But one man did not join the general exhilaration. He was the same thin man, the host's best friend. Instead of scratching his chin, the thin man began now to rub the tip of his nose with his middle finger.

"What about wind?" the thin man asked, his finger stopping dead on its course. "What about wind?" again the chorus. "The wind can chase clouds, for heaven's sake!"

"That's true enough," the host again admitted, regretfully. "All right," he added after a pause.

The thin man turned to him with a startled look. "What did you say?"

"All right," the cat owner repeated.

"All right what?" The thin man was flabbergasted.

"All right, Wind. I like it. I will call her Wind then."

Again, the ear-splitting applause. Spotting the lovely cat passing through the front porch, one man even called to her "Wind! Wind! Come on in here for a minute. Wind!"

One hand shot out, fingers spread. It was the thin man. "No, no, no," he said, shaking his gaunt face sadly. His eyes were deluged with sorrow. "And what about wall? A wall can stop the wind!"

The host hastened to accept the inevitable. "I will call my cat Wall then!" he said. But apparently his good will did not make any visible impression upon his best friend, for the latter only shook his head. Sadly he looked at the others.

"Yes, Wall, that's a nice name. Wall, yes," he mused aloud. "But, but mice can bore holes through a wall, yes, they can," he burst out.

"I will call her Mouse! That settles it! My Mouse! My dear little Mouse!" roared the delighted host, clasping the thin man's arm in a show of appreciation. He turned toward his other guests. But all looked thoughtful and sad this time. For all knew what could catch a mouse. Our host's grin froze into a grimace.

"All right, all right, I will call my cat Cat then," he declared. "A cat is a cat is a cat!" Happiness was instantly reestablished. The host ordered his wife to bring out a whole new jar of rice wine. The occasion deserved it.

The good man's wife, however, told a neighbor that in the evening, when no one is around, her husband still calls his cat . . . Heaven!

THE GOLDEN BUFFALO

◎◎◎◎◎

IN THE early eleventh century, when Viet-Nam was ruled by the Ly dynasty, there lived a Buddhist monk whose name was Khong-Lo. It was widely believed that heaven had sent this venerable one to help people. The belief was not without reason: the monk was known to possess extraordinary powers. He could stop a hurricane in its destructive course; he could call for the rain when a drought was too severe. It was said that, more than once, with a touch of his fingers he made a paralytic walk, and he had given the gift of speech back to a mute just by talking to him.

At this time, Khong-Lo was a very old man. But although his hair was all white, his face remained youthful and unlined. The contrast was awe-inspiring. It was as if eternal youth and ageless wisdom were mingled together. Always alone, he wandered from village to village, from town to town. Everywhere he stopped, people quickly gathered around him. Seated under a tree, the monk would give advice, settle disputes, heal the sick, aid the poor. Khong-Lo's fame spread far and wide. He was a saint whom the people could see with their own eyes, touch with their own hands.

Then one day, the great monk started out for China, and this last exploit in the land of the Middle Flower has been told and retold for almost ten centuries.

After months of traveling across mountains and rivers, the monk arrived at the Chinese capital. The great Sung dynasty was then the reigning imperial house. But the splendors and riches of the Chinese people did not impress the monk who asked to be received by the Emperor himself. Amazingly, his wish was granted without delay.

"Glory to Your Majesty!" said the humble monk to the Chinese "Son of Heaven" when he was brought before him. "I have come here all the way from Viet-Nam with only a little request. Time and again your great Middle Kingdom has invaded my small and modest homeland, and time and again your brave officers and troops have taken back to China innumerable goods. Viet-Nam has lost gold and silver by the tons, iron and copper by the shipfuls, rice by the millions of bushels and cattle by thousands of heads. Now I have come here, as a poor Viet-Namese monk, with only one wish, which I beg Your Majesty to fulfill."

When the monk was ordered to express his wish, he pulled from inside his sleeve a little cloth bag: "I would like, Your Majesty, to fill this bag with whatever I choose to take from your vaults and coffers. I will take only this bagful of treasure, no more, back to my people."

Accompanied by a treasurer-officer, Khong-Lo made his way through the endless underground corridors of the vaults. He passed doors marked Gold, Silver, Pearls, Emeralds, Rubies, Diamonds . . . but to the Chinese officer's puzzlement did not pause once. After what seemed to be miles of corridors, the two men arrived at an immense chamber whose entrance was guarded by a gigantic buffalo of solid gold. Inside, the chamber seemed all but empty; only a large pile of some kind of metal lay in the middle of the marble floor. As soon as he was within reach of this metal, however, the monk began to fill his little cloth bag with it.

Immediately the Chinese officer tried to prevent him saying, "No, you must not take this. This is black gold. This is the mother of yellow gold and is infinitely more precious."

"I know it," the monk replied with dignity. "That's why I am taking some of it back to my people. Have you forgotten His Majesty's order? I am allowed to take anything from his treasuries. Look, my little bag is not even filled up yet!" And it was true, his bag was not full although many black gold ingots had been stuffed into it.

So, on and on the monk kept filling it, and yet the bag was not full. Realizing suddenly that he was unable to deal with such a supernatural man, the Chinese officer turned and ran for help. As soon as the Emperor heard the story, he ordered the monk arrested. But when the soldiers arrived at the chamber, the monk was nowhere to be found. And the pile of priceless black gold in the middle of the marble floor was reduced to one half.

Taking different routes to the sea, the various detachments of mounted soldiers pursued the fugitive. Those who arrived at the seashore first were nevertheless too late. They reached the water only to witness a most incredible feat. Laughing merrily, Khong-Lo was sitting in his very own straw hat, which, turned upside down, conveniently served as a boat. The hat was barely as large as a palm leaf but it floated atop the foaming waves as if the old monk and his bag of gold weighed nothing at all.

When Khong-Lo was once again in Viet-Nam, he gave the black gold to the best metal workers in the country. He had decided that the best use of this precious gold would be to make an immense bell which would belong to everyone in the land.

When completed, the bell was beyond compare. It was immense in size, incredible in workmanship, beautiful in shape and adornment. Installed on the bank of the Western Lake of the capital city, it was ready to make its first thunderous sounds.

The great day soon arrived. Men, women, and children massed around the lake in circles which stretched for miles. In the presence of the King's envoy, the dignitaries, and the people, the old monk, in his humble brown robe, grasped the huge wooden mallet with both hands, and slanting his frail body forward, hit the bell with all his strength.

The bell's sound rose in the sky like a melodious storm, full yet clear, loud yet grave, immense yet tender. It rolled out from the bell like waves from the bottom of the ocean, one after another, endless, everlasting. Thousands of people instinctively closed their eyes in order to better enjoy the sound which traveled across the sky to the very limits of the horizon and died away like minute golden threads.

And then thousands of eyes opened. A strange noise was heard amidst the bell's beautiful song. Clouds parted, thunder rolled, lightning sparkled. The strange sound became louder and louder, and everyone knew that it was the galloping of some large, hoofed animal. The sun suddenly brightened as if a thousand suns had come together, and in the north, there appeared a huge golden buffalo, galloping, galloping at great speed through the parting clouds. Everyone froze in consternation and terror.

Khong-Lo alone kept calm. Staring at the oncoming monster, he suddenly slapped his forehead. "Of course!" he exclaimed. "Of course!" And without waiting a moment the old monk rolled up his flowing sleeves, grasped the huge bell with both arms, tore it free from the ropes holding it to the enormous bell columns, and in one incredible heave, rolled it over and over into the lake.

Before the water's surface had had time to still, it broke apart again. Arriving like a hurricane, glittering more than the sun itself, the golden buffalo plunged headlong into the lake and disappeared with the bell. . . .

Long after this happened, the old monk also disappeared and no one ever saw him again. It is said that when he saw the monster coming over the clouds, Khong-Lo recognized it as the Golden Buffalo, guardian of the Emperor of China's treasure vaults, and immediately understood the reason for its appearance. The bell was made of black gold, and the buffalo of yellow gold. Since black gold was the mother of yellow gold, the Golden Buffalo naturally hurried to come when the bell was struck to answer its mother's call. The monk feared that if the bell remained any longer, all the gold of China would soon rush south to Viet-Nam. China and Viet-Nam would then be at war again. That was why Khong-Lo hurriedly and single-handedly threw the bell into the lake.

DRAGONS ?

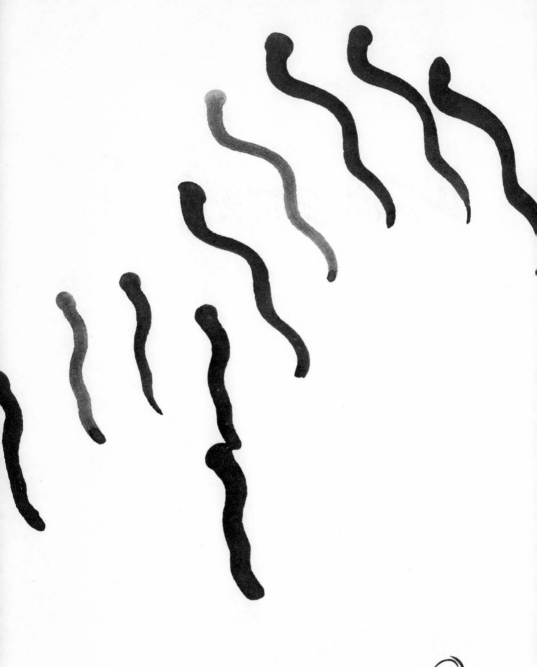

◎◎◎◎◎

Once upon a time in Viet-Nam, there was a man named Kinh. Mr. Kinh was a very quick man. How quick is shown by the following story:

AMONG the Chinese residents of the capital city was a famous painter. Not only did this foreigner paint beautiful pictures, but he also painted very fast. People who had had the opportunity to watch him paint said that their eyes were barely able to follow his hand, it moved so quickly. He could, they said, cover square yards of paper with mountains and rivers, beasts and men, in less time than it takes a tea lover to empty a cup of tea.

It was even said that once with brush ready in hand he had sketched flying fish while they were in mid-air! With such performances to his credit, this Chinese used to say that between sky and earth he was the greatest, the fastest painter alive.

Even though he lived in a small hamlet, far away from the capital, Mr. Kinh had heard these tales. Since he himself was fond of dabbling in ink, Mr. Kinh decided to go see the Chinese master for himself.

Brought into the great man's presence, Mr. Kinh said to him: "Sir, I have heard of your extraordinary talent as an artist and as a fast artist. I came here with only one modest request . . ."

"Yes, yes," the Chinese painter encouraged the man. "What is it that is in your mind, most honorable visitor?"

"I wish to see you paint, sir," Mr. Kinh said.   The Chinese official laughed kindly: "But that is simple enough. I shall satisfy your heart's desire! Servants! Bring ink and brushes!"

But Mr. Kinh began to scratch his temple (a Viet-Namese sign of embarrassment or perplexity): "But, sir," he said to the Chinese, "I would like to paint too."

"You would!" the great man was taken aback. "You mean," he asked after a moment, "you mean you would like to compete with me?"

"That's right, sir, that's right. Please forgive my brashness . . ." Mr. Kinh sighed while the Chinese artist looked at him in amusement, in disbelief, almost in pity.

When the inkwells, brushes and paper were all laid out on opposite mats, the two men took their places. Outside, on the stone steps of the mansion, a servant was standing ready by a large drum, drumstick in hand.

It was agreed that at the first sound of the drum, they would begin painting, and each would have to finish his picture before the drumroll was over.

The great Chinese artist asked Mr. Kinh: "Now, honorable visitor, what would you like to choose as the subject of our painting?"

Mr. Kinh looked up and down and around the large chamber. His eyes fell on the intricately carved beam overhead. It was a colossal hunk of wood, lacquered in red with gold dragons coiling around it. "We shall paint dragons," Mr. Kinh declared.

Ordered to beat the drum, the servant raised his arm and the two men began to work.

The Chinese was an extraordinary sight. His right hand flew from the inkwell to the paper and back so fast that it became only a blur. His eyes flashed, his hair swung; one would think he was in the act of becoming a dragon himself. And like magic, the dragon he was painting appeared almost complete on the paper, surrounded by clouds and lightning, its jaws gaping, its nostrils breathing fire, its claws quivering. . . .

Then triumphantly, the famous painter stopped, threw his brush into the brush holder and sat back. Outside the first drum-roll was still softly dying away.

But the great man's face clouded over and his smile froze into a grimace. The Viet-Namese visitor, with folded arms, was looking at him.

"Have you finished?" the Chinese inquired brusquely.

"Yes, sir, I have. A long time ago. I have been watching you paint. You were magnificent," Mr. Kinh replied.

"But, but," the Chinese lost his patience, "but you have finished your picture before me!"

"Yes, sir, I have," the Viet-Namese said. "I have painted not one but *ten* dragons."

And when the Chinese painter saw what was on his competitor's sheet of paper, he could not help letting out an astonished, "Oh!" But he stood up, solemnly bent down and bowed low to Mr. Kinh, expressing thus, in oriental fashion, respect and admiration.

On Mr. Kinh's picture, there was nothing but ten short wriggling black lines.

As Mr. Kinh told it later, when the drumroll began he quickly dipped all ten fingertips onto the inkstone and brought them dripping over his sheet of rice paper. Mr. Kinh knew, and knew that his Chinese host knew, that in the Chinese language earthworms are called of all things, earthdragons!

About the Author

Vo-Dinh was born in Hue, the former imperial capital of Viet-Nam. He studied at the Lycée of Hue, and at the Sorbonne, the Académie de la Grande Chaumière, and the Ecole Nationale Supérieure des Beaux-Arts in Paris.

Mr. Vo-Dinh is a professional artist whose oils and woodcuts have been exhibited in twelve one-man shows both here and abroad. He has also illustrated books, UNICEF greeting cards, and a collection of haiku for children, BIRDS, FROGS, AND MOONLIGHT.

He lives in Matamoras, Pennsylvania, with his wife and two daughters, Phuong-Nam and Linh-Giang.